A preliminary evaluation of the status of shark species

380

by
José I. Castro
Christa M. Woodley
and
Rebecca L. Brudek
National Oceanographic and Atmospheric Administration
National Marine Fisheries Service
Southeast Fisheries Science Center
Miami, Florida
USA

Food
and
Agriculture
Organization
of
the
United
Nations

Rome, 1999

M-40
ISBN 92-5-104299-3

PREPARATION OF THIS DOCUMENT

This survey was undertaken at the request of FAO in 1996. The evaluation is based upon a survey of the scientific literature, on unpublished data made available to us by several researchers or institutions, and on a questionnaire on biological and fishery data on shark sent out to national institutions. Because of the wide or cosmopolitan ranges of many species of sharks, and because of the lack of fisheries data, in most cases it was not possible to assess a species as a whole.

Much of the data used in this report is of Australian or of North American origin. This is simply a reflection of the effort spent in shark research and management in Australia and, in the last few years, in the United States.

As a survey of the status of all the shark species, this work can be considered only as a preliminary assessment, as it reflects our fragmentary knowledge of sharks and the paucity of fisheries data that was available to the authors. Many species are simply listed as being *Category 1*, corresponding to exploited species for which biological or fishery data are few or non existent. It is hoped that this preliminary assessment will encourage others to make the relevant data available to FAO for inclusion in future revisions.

ACKNOWLEDGEMENTS

We thank Merri Camhi, Geremy Cliff, and Bill Richards for comments on the manuscript. We thank Josh Bennet, Greg Cailliet, Joao Correia, Sheldon Dudley, Robert Hueter, Oistein Jakobsen, Marcel Kroese, Gerry Scott, Paddy Walker, and Terry Walker for species and/or fishery data. We depended on two sterling librarians who unearthed many difficult-to-find references: Harriet Corvino at the Southeast Fisheries Science Center, and Jean Collins at FAO, Rome. Their help was simply splendid. We are most grateful to Richard Grainger of FAO for all his wonderful logistical help during the project, and for his hospitality to the senior author during his visits to Rome. This project could not have been accomplished without his guidance and help. We are also grateful to the anonymous reviewer who suggested the status categories used here, solving a thorny problem.

This is contribution No. PRD-97/98-20 of the Protected Resources and Biodiversity Division of the Southeast Fisheries Science Center, NMFS, NOAA.

Castro, J.I. ; Woodley, C.M. ; Brudek, R.L.
A preliminary evaluation of the status of shark species.
FAO Fisheries Technical Paper. No. 380. Rome, FAO. 1999. 72p.

ABSTRACT

The status of shark species is reviewed based on the available data. A review of the history of shark fisheries demonstrates that intensive shark fisheries are not sustainable. Numerous problems are encountered in assessing shark populations: a general lack of biological and fishery data, lack of suitable models, and lack of validated age estimates. Sharks have an unusual combination of biological characteristics: slow growth and delayed maturation, long reproductive cycles, low fecundity and long life spans. These characteristics make them vulnerable to overfishing. A preliminary evaluation of the status of shark species is made on the basis of historical data, the reproductive potential of each species, and the level of exploitation of the species. In this document, exploited shark species are classified numerically according to their vulnerability. The majority of these species are listed as Category 1, indicating that there are not sufficient data to assess the species. Available data indicate that sharks are very vulnerable and are threatened by overexploitation in many parts of the world.

Distribution:

Marine sciences
Directors of Fisheries
FAO Regional Fishery Offices
FAO Fisheries Department

CONTENTS

1. Introduction

In November 1994, the Convention on International Trade in Endangered Species (CITES) passed a resolution requesting that the Food and Agriculture Organization of the United Nations (FAO) and other international organizations to establish programmes to collect and assemble the necessary biological and trade data on sharks. This CITES resolution reflects the concern that shark stocks are being depleted rapidly and an attempt must be made to understand and quantify the effects of the world trade on shark populations. The purpose of this work is to indicate the species of sharks that may be threatened by overexploitation or trade, in response to the CITES request. This work lists all species of sharks that are reported in both commercial and recreational fisheries throughout the world, and assigns a status category to each, based on historical fishery trends, on reproductive potential of the species, and on the impact of fisheries upon the species. The authors believe that a species approach is the only meaningful and practical approach to shark conservation and management. Generic compilations of elasmobranch or "shark" landings, although interesting, convey little understanding of what is happening to species in a fishery, and are of little practical use in management and conservation attempts.

1.1 HISTORICAL BACKGROUND

In the early 1980s, political and economic changes throughout the world affected fishing markets and operations. In particular in China, shark fins were no longer considered as a luxury product and it led to a significant growth of domestic consumption thanks also to the reduction of tariff rates on imported shark fins (Cook 1990, Rose 1996). In other areas, declining catches and rising prices of traditional food fishes made under-utilized sharks an inexpensive source of protein. These two factors engendered numerous and diverse shark fisheries throughout the world. By the late 1980s, shark fisheries everywhere were growing at a rapid pace fuelled by the demand and the high shark fin prices. By the mid 1990s, the ex-vessel price for dry shark fins had reached US $60 per kilogram, providing sufficient incentive to harvest sharks, even when the meat was not marketable. Currently, shark fisheries encompass the entire world and catch most large species of coastal and oceanic sharks.

While shark fisheries were growing in the early 1980s, the pelagic swordfish and tuna longline fisheries were also growing dramatically. These fisheries normally catch a large proportion of sharks as bycatch. In the early years of those fisheries, sharks were usually released or discarded. By the late 1980s, the high price of the fins caused previously released or discarded sharks to be retained as bycatch, and to be brought on board to be finned. Today, shark bycatch is probably a significant portion of the total shark mortality.

The history of the shark fisheries indicates that intensive fisheries are not sustainable, and that initial exploitation is followed by, at best, a rapid decline in catch rates or, at worst, by a complete collapse of the fishery (Holden 1974). Examples of shark fisheries that collapsed are the California soupfin shark fishery (Ripley 1946), the New England porbeagle fishery (Casey et al. 1978), the Australian school shark fishery (Olsen 1954), the English basking shark fishery (Parker and Stott 1965), and the California thresher shark fishery (Cailliet et al. 1991). Once a shark fishery has collapsed, it takes many decades for the stocks to recover, if they recover at all.

In the past, most shark fisheries were small artisanal fisheries that caught whatever species of sharks were locally or seasonally abundant, or intensive regional fisheries that targeted individual species for specific products: liver oil in the cases of the soupfin and basking sharks, and meat in the cases of the porbeagle and school sharks. Fishery administrators and the public generally had little interest in shark fisheries, because they were usually small. The rapid growth in the size and value of the shark fisheries throughout the world, along with increasing shark bycatch and recreational fishing, and the known vulnerability of sharks to overfishing, have engendered worldwide concerns and attempts to manage and conserve sharks. In addition to the economic concerns for a valuable resource, public attitude towards sharks in some countries has changed dramatically. The conservation ethic and concern for wildlife have been extended to encompass sharks, and, in many parts of the world, the public has developed an acute interest in conserving sharks.

Attempts to manage or conserve sharks have been few, and usually engendered by economic concerns about declining fisheries. Australia has had a shark fishery since the turn of the century, and it imposed more restrictions on licenses and fishing methods in 1988 (Stevens 1993). The sand tiger shark, *Carcharias taurus,* received protected status in the Australian state of New South Wales in 1984 (Pollard 1996). In New Zealand, shark management started in 1986 over concerns of declining catch per unit effort (CPUE). In South Africa, the great white shark has been protected since 1991 (Compagno 1991). In the United States, concerns about a rapidly growing fishery and overfishing led to a fishery management plan for the Atlantic coast in 1993 (NMFS 1993). Protected status has been given in April 1997 to five species in the United States on the Atlantic coast: the great white shark; the whale shark; the basking shark; the sand tiger shark; and the bigeye sand tiger shark. Shark fisheries along the western coast of the United States for shortfin mako and thresher sharks have been regulated by state agencies for many years. In 1989, the states of California, Oregon and Washington enacted an inter-jurisdictional fishery-monitoring plan for thresher sharks (Hanan *et al.* 1993).

2. Problems in understanding and assessing the status of shark populations

We encountered several problems in determining the impact of trade upon species of sharks. First, there is a general lack of biological knowledge about sharks. Second, we encountered a general lack of species-specific catch and effort statistics in the shark fisheries and in the shark bycatch. Third, the specific data needed for demographic and stock assessment models is simply lacking and most of the models used in stock assessment were developed for bony fishes and their application to sharks may be questionable. Below are the explanations for these generalized problems.

Lack of biological data: There are several reasons for the scarcity of basic biological knowledge on sharks and elasmobranchs, in general. In the past, there was little economic incentive or impetus to study sharks. The low value of shark meat was greatly exceeded by that of many teleosts (e.g., tunas, mackerels, snappers, groupers, etc.), thus the impetus was on elucidating the biology of valuable teleosts. Furthermore, prior to the emergence of the commercial shark fisheries of the middle 1980s, most students were discouraged from studying sharks by the logistical problems encountered trying to obtain specimens. As a result, most ichthyologists and fishery scientists studied teleosts and ignored sharks. Consequently, only a handful of the species of sharks involved in intensive fisheries in developed countries were studied. This situation has been changing in the last decade, because the increase in value of shark products and the ecological concerns about sharks. However, due to scarce research money and logistical problems, progress in shark biology continues to be slow.

Lack of fisheries data: Lack of fishery data on shark fisheries is critical to their proper assessment. Obtaining data is difficult, for the following reasons:

- Most fisheries simply do not report shark landings by species. They usually lump together all shark species and often all elasmobranchs are included together. The reasons for this practice are the lack of trained personnel capable of discriminating among species, and the lack of incentive to produce shark statistics. In most cases, we do not have catch or landings statistics by species, or by higher taxonomic level, to quantify fishing mortality of a given species of shark or species complex. The interpretation of the available generic data is difficult, since the catch species composition is not known. Even when the present catch composition is known, and good time series are available, one can not extrapolate the composition of past generalized landings, because one can not assume that the catch species composition has remained unchanged through time.

- Effort data are usually missing in fishery statistics, making the interpretation of landings statistics difficult.

- In the few cases where fisheries do have good statistics, they are often reluctant to publish such data, because they fear that restrictions will be placed on their fishing activities.

- The migratory patterns of some targeted sharks species complicate the analysis of fisheries data. They are caught by various fisheries in two or more countries, making it difficult to determine the total catch or the age structure of the total catch.

It is unlikely that the present lack of fishery data will change in the near future, because many countries simply lack the resources and infrastructure to monitor their fisheries adequately. It will take a concerted effort by interested countries and international agencies to improve the training of fishery workers in shark or elasmobranch identification before meaningful statistics on shark catches and landings can be expected.

Lack of suitable models: We lack the suitable population models to assess the impact of fishing and trade on sharks, and we do not know the sizes of shark populations or stocks. Most of the theoretical stock assessment models are based on bony fishes with life histories that are quite different from sharks. Consequently, attempts at shark stock assessment have been few and the results have been questionable or severely flawed. In recent years, demographic analysis has been used to analyze the effects of fishing upon shark populations. Only a handful of species have been analyzed (e.g., Cortés 1995, Sminkey and Musick 1995) and in most cases, the parameters necessary for analysis, such as age at maturity, mortality, etc., are not known.

Lack of validated age estimates: The growth rate of a species and its estimated age at sexual maturity are essential for stock assessment and demographic models. Information on growth of elasmobranchs has been derived from counts of opaque and translucent bands ("rings") in their spines and vertebrae, because elasmobranchs lack the hard parts (scales, otoliths, or bones) commonly used in age and growth studies of teleosts (Cailliet *et al.* 1986). Although, the mechanism of calcium deposition in these bands is not understood, the periodicity of these bands is usually taken as an indicator of annual growth. However, in some cases, such as in the basking shark, two such bands appear to be deposited each year (Parker and Stott 1965), and in the case of the angel shark, band deposition has been shown to be more closely related to somatic growth than to age (Natanson and Cailliet 1990). A few elasmobranch studies have evaluated the temporal periodicity of the band deposition in the spines and vertebral centra (Beamish and McFarlane 1983, Cailliet *et al.* 1986), and ever fewer have validated the age estimates. To our knowledge, no author has validated *different* age groups of any elasmobranch species, thus assuming that the rate of deposition is the same before and after maturity, when the growth rate changes abruptly. The extrapolation beyond the maximum age validated, between species, or between populations of the same species is, as Beamish and McFarlane (1983) stated, "dangerous".

Because of the limitations outlined above, the assessment of the status of shark species can be made on historical data (catches, landings, CPUE, etc.) in only a few cases. In the cases where fishery data do not exist, the status can be inferred from the unique characteristics of sharks, the reproductive potential of the species, growth coefficients, and from the level of exploitation being applied. These factors are explained below.

3. Biological characteristics and reproductive potential of sharks

Most sharks have an unusual combination of biological characteristics: slow growth and delayed maturation; long reproductive cycles; low fecundity; and long life spans. These factors determine the low reproductive potential of many shark species.

Slow growth and delayed maturation: Some species of sharks, including some of the commercially important species, are extremely slow growing. The picked dogfish (*Squalus acanthias*) has been estimated by Jones and Geen (1977) to reach maturity at about 25 years. The sandbar shark (*Carcharhinus plumbeus*), the most economically important species along the southeastern coast of the United States, has been estimated to reach maturity from 15-16 years (Sminkey and Musick 1995) to about 30 years (Casey and Natanson 1992).

Long reproductive cycles: Sharks produce young that hatch or are born fully developed, and that are relatively large at hatching or birth. The energy requirements of producing large, fully developed young result in great energy demands on the female, and in reproductive cycles and gestation periods that are unusually long for fishes. Both the reproductive cycle and the gestation period usually last one or two years in most species of sharks, reflecting the time it takes a female to store enough energy to produce large eggs and to nurture her large young through development (Castro 1996). The reproductive cycle is how often the shark reproduces, and it is usually one or two years long. The gestation period is the time of embryonic development from fertilization to birth, and is frequently one or two years long. The reproductive cycle and the gestation period may run concurrently or consecutively. For example, in the picked dogfish, the reproductive cycle and gestation run concurrently and both last two years. A female carries both developing oocytes in the ovary and developing embryos in the uteri concurrently for two years. Shortly after parturition, it mates and ovulates again, and the process begins anew. In this case, both ovulation and parturition are biennial. In most of the large, commercially important, carcharhinid sharks, the reproductive cycle and the gestation period run consecutively. These sharks have biennial reproductive cycles (Clark and von Schmidt 1965) with one-year gestation cycles. They accumulate the energy reserves necessary to produce large eggs for about a year, then, mate, ovulate, gestate for one year, and give birth. For example, after giving birth in the spring, a blacktip shark (*Carcharhinus limbatus*) enters a "resting" stage where it stores energy and nourishes its large oocytes for one year. After mating and ovulation, it begins a year gestation period, giving birth in the spring of the second year after its previous parturition (Castro 1996). Thus, these sharks also reproduce biennially. Some of the hammerhead sharks (*Sphyrna*) and the sharpnose sharks (*Rhizoprionodon*) reproduce annually (Castro 1989, Castro and Wourms 1993). Even longer cycles of three and four years have been proposed for other species without adducing any evidence.

Low fecundity: The small size of their broods, or "litters", is another factor contributing to the low reproductive potential of sharks. The number of young or "pups" per brood usually ranges from two to a dozen, although some species may produce dozens of young per brood. Most of the commercially important carcharhinid sharks usually produce less than a dozen young per brood. For example, the sandbar shark averages 8 young per brood, while the blacktip averages 4 per brood (Castro 1996). An exception, among the targeted species, is the blue shark for which broods of over 30 young have often been reported.

Long life spans: Although, many species of sharks are known to be long-lived (Pratt and Casey 1990), the reproductive life span of sharks is unknown. Because the long time before maturation and the long reproductive cycles, it appears that a given female may only produce a few broods in its lifetime (Sminkey and Musick 1995).

Many of the commercially important species use shallow coastal waters, known as "nurseries", to give birth to their young, and where the young spend their first months or years (Castro 1993b). The mating grounds are often close to the nurseries, and thus adults of both sexes congregate close to shore in large numbers. These areas are highly attractive to fishermen, because of their nearness to shore and the high concentration of sharks. Most of the commercially important species (e.g. the genera *Carcharhinus, Sphyrna, Rhizoprionodon, Negaprion*) have shallow water nurseries (Castro 1987, 1993b). These sharks are very vulnerable to modern fishing operations, and are easily overfished.

There is no evidence of any compensatory mechanisms by female sharks that will increase brood size or decrease the length of the ovarian and gestation cycles in response to overfishing. It is highly unlikely that those mechanisms can be evolved rapidly enough to compensate for the increase in mortality. Even if such mechanisms could be evolved, brood size would be limited by the maximum number of young that can be carried by a female, and ovulatory and gestation cycles are limited by complex metabolic processes. The long ovarian cycles and long gestation periods probably reflect he minimal times required by the species to acquire and transfer the necessary energy to large ova and young.

4. The status of elasmobranch species

We have evaluated the status of all valid species of sharks listed by Compagno (1984) with a few additions or changes. The data used in our assessment came from various sources: published literature, FAO reports, responses to FAO inquiries, and expert consultations. We have relied heavily on the original published literature, specifically on data published in refereed, scientific literature. We considered such data to be the most reliable and have avoided "grey literature" of popular articles, personal reports by the unqualified, etc. Whenever needed we have provided citations to justify our statements.

The categories we propose indicate species vulnerability and they are precautionary. Under the precautionary approach, the absence of adequate scientific information cannot be used as a reason to postpone or fail to take conservation and management measures (see FAO Code of Conduct for Responsible Fisheries, paragraph 7.5.1). Because of the lack of data, we have interpreted this as allowing small amounts of information to allocate categories where concern is warranted. The onus is therefore on obtaining more and better data to improve the category status of individual species.

For the purposes of assigning status categories, the species are divided into two groups: "Not-exploited species " and "Exploited species". In turn, the "Exploited species" are divided into five numerical categories. We are aware of the problems of a numerical classification, and would have preferred to use the widely employed categories and terminology of the International Union for Conservation of Nature and Natural Resources (IUCN) Red List. However, the lack of knowledge of population size, generation time, etc., and the widespread ranges of many sharks preclude the meaningful use of that classification. Thus, we used a separate classification simply to avoid confusion with the IUCN and other classification systems. The categories used in this work and their criteria are explained below.

4.1 EXPLANATION OF THE STATUS CATEGORIES

A. Not-exploited species: Species that are not currently targeted by fisheries, and that are not normally found in the bycatch of any fisheries.

B. Exploited species: Species that are directly exploited by fisheries or taken as bycatch.

> **Category 1:** Exploited species that can not be placed on any of the subsequent categories, because of lack of data.

> **Category 2:** Species pursued in directed fisheries, and/or regularly found in bycatch, whose catches have not decreased historically, probably due to their higher reproductive potential.

> **Category 3:** Species that are exploited by directed fisheries or bycatch, and have a limited reproductive potential, and/or other life history characteristics that make them especially vulnerable to overfishing, and/or that are being fished in their nursery areas.

> **Category 4:** Species in this category show substantial historical declines in catches and/or have become locally extinct.

> **Category 5:** Species that have become rare throughout the ranges where they were formerly abundant, based on historical records, catch statistics, or expert's reports.

Because of the widespread ranges or cosmopolitan distribution of many elasmobranchs, one can distinguish between "local extinction" and "extinction". Local extinction refers to the disappearance of a species or population in a given geographic area, while the species is still extant in the rest of its range. Extinction refers to the disappearance of the species in a global scale. These two terms must be used with caution, because we do not know the nature and extent of shark stocks. Some species or stocks may have entire ocean basins as their ranges. Overfishing and depletion in one part of the range may have significant effects on the whole population which may be difficult to detect, because of the deficiencies of shark fishery data. There are few recorded cases of local extinction of sharks or elasmobranchs, in general. Quero and Emonnet (1993) documented the disappearance of the bramble shark off France after centuries of bycatch. Brander (1981) reported that the common skate (*Raia batis*) had declined in abundance in the Irish Sea, and that the species had been brought to the "edge of extinction" by commercial fishing. The extinction on a global scale of widely distributed or cosmopolitan elasmobranchs has not been demonstrated yet. Nevertheless, it is possible that given enough time and sufficient fishing pressure, some sharks could become globally extinct.

The categories do not distinguish between the effects of artisanal fisheries and modern intensive fisheries. The widespread use of the monofilament gillnet in artisanal fisheries has changed the efficiency of those fisheries. Whereas industrial fisheries may cease to operate when catches fall to low levels, artisanal fisheries may continue as their operational costs are much lower. The effects on elasmobranch populations appear to be similar in either type of fishery.

4.2 SPECIES ACCOUNTS BY FAMILY

Each exploited species is described in a brief synopsis. The species synopses contain the following:

a) A brief statement or summary of the biology and range of a species. *This section is purposely brief.* Readers desiring more information can turn to many excellent monographs on sharks (e.g. Bigelow and Schroeder 1948, Cadenat and Blache 1981, Bass *et al.* 1973, Compagno 1984, Last and Stevens 1994)

b) A description of the reproductive potential of a species, providing information on growth rates, age and size at maturity, size of young, size of broods, longevity, and location of nursery areas. These data can be used to estimate how a given species will respond to exploitation. It would have been preferable to calculate reproductive potential based on a formula using growth coefficients, reproductive rate, mortality, etc. Such a formula has not been devised or agreed upon for sharks, and if it existed, we would lack the necessary data for most species.

c) Documentation of the impact of fisheries, and how the species has reacted to exploitation in those fisheries.

d) A status category for each species based on historical fishery trends, its reproductive potential, and the level of exploitation. The status categories reflect how a given species has reacted to exploitation at a given locality and its vulnerability to fisheries.

4.2.1 Frilled shark, Family Chlamydoselachidae

Frilled shark (*Chlamydoselachus anguineus*)

The frilled shark, the only living member of the family, is a rare deep-water shark of worldwide distribution. It is a scarcely caught fish, usually found in water 550-900 m. It is generally protected from fisheries by its deep-water habitat and scarcity.

Status: Not-exploited species.

4.2.2 Cow sharks, Family Hexanchidae

The cow shark family includes the sixgill and sevengill sharks, a small group of primarily deep-water species of wide distribution. There are four species, three are bathyal and one is neritic.

Sharpnose sevengill shark (*Heptranchias perlo*)

This is a deep-water species of the continental shelves, where it appears to be most common at depths of 180-450 m. It has worldwide distribution in deep tropical and warm temperate waters. Very little is known of its habits (Castro 1983).

Reproductive potential: Maturity is reached at about 85-90 cm TL. Broods consist of 9-20 young, which measure about 25 cm TL at birth (Castro 1983). According to Tanaka and Mizue (1977), off Kyushu, Japan, the species reproduces all year round. The lengths of the reproductive and gestation cycles are unknown.

Impact of fisheries: The sharpnose sevengill shark is sometimes caught in large numbers as bycatch in fisheries using bottom trawls or longlines (Compagno 1984). In North America, it is occasionally seen in small numbers as bycatch of tilefish longlines (Castro unpublished data).

Status: Category 1. There are not sufficient data to evaluate the impact of bycatch.

Bluntnose sixgill shark (*Hexanchus griseus*)

This is a common, bottom-dwelling, species usually reported from depths of 180-1100 m, in deep tropical and temperate waters throughout the world (Castro 1983). It often comes close to the surface at night, where it may take longlines set for other species. Juveniles stray into very shallow cool waters. This is one of the largest sharks.

Reproductive potential: Very few mature bluntnose sixgill sharks have been examined by biologists, thus the reproductive processes are poorly known. Ebert (1986) reported a 421 cm TL female to be gravid with term embryos. Harvey-Clark (1995) stated that males mature at 325 cm TL, without adducing any evidence for this. The species has not been aged. It is probably long-lived, like the Greenland shark, another deep-water giant shark, but there is no evidence for this. The young measure 60-70 cm TL at birth. Broods are large, up to 108 young have been reported (Castro 1983).

Impact of fisheries: Juveniles are common in deep continental waters and often enter coastal waters; however, the adults are seldom taken (Springer and Waller 1969, Ebert 1986). Apparently, adults are in waters deeper than those regularly fished, or perhaps they break the gear and escape. Thus, the very deep habitat of the adults, or perhaps their large size, seems to convey some measure of protection from most fisheries. According to Harvey-Clark (1995), the bluntnose sixgill shark became the target of a directed, subsidized, longline fishery off British Columbia, Canada, in 1991. At about the same time, the species also became of interest as an ecotourism resource, with several companies taking diving tourists to watch sixgill sharks in their environment. The fishery was unregulated, and lasted until 1993, when the commercial harvest of bluntnose sixgill sharks was discontinued due to conservation and management concerns. According to Harvey-Clark (1995), diver observations of sharks decreased in 1993 and it was unclear at the time whether the fishery or the ecotourism could be sustained. A fishery for bluntnose sixgill sharks started in the Maldives in 1980, peaked in 1982-84, and had collapsed by 1996 (Letter from Murray Johns, Ministry of Fisheries and Agriculture, Republic of Maldives, to FAO on 9 Oct. 1996).

Status: Category 3. It is difficult to evaluate the bluntnose sixgill shark, because the lack of fisheries or landings data. The species may be very vulnerable to overfishing.

Bigeyed sixgill shark (*Hexanchus vitulus*)

This is a poorly known deep-water shark that was not described until 1969. Most specimens have been accidental captures at depths of 400 m in tropical waters (Castro 1983).

Status: Not-exploited species.

Broadnose sevengill shark (*Notorynchus cepedianus*)

The broadnose sevengill shark is wide-ranging mostly in temperate seas (Compagno 1984). It is primarily a large coastal species often found in shallow water. Frequently, it is the top predator in this shallow environment. It is of local economic importance. In California, it is considered one of the most palatable sharks. In spite of its widespread abundance, it is a very poorly known species.

Reproductive potential: According to Ebert (1989), males over 150 cm TL are mature, and females mature at 250 cm TL and weigh more than 91 kg. A gravid female contained 83 eggs, indicating that broods are large (Herald 1968). The reproductive cycle appears to be biennial (Ebert 1989). The species has not been aged due to lack of calcification of the vertebrae (Ebert 1989). The nursery areas are in shallow coastal bays, such as San Francisco and Monterey bays in California, USA (Castro 1983).

Impact of fisheries: The large size, local abundance, and high-quality flesh of these sharks make it the subject of fisheries in several areas where it occurs. In California, USA, and southern Australia it is fished by sport and commercial fishermen for human consumption (Compagno 1984). In Argentina, it is often caught in tope gillnets (G. Chiaramonte pers. comm.).

Status: Category 1. There is little data to evaluate the impact of fisheries upon the broadnose sevengill. In California, broadnose sevengill shark landings are often combined with those of the bluntnose sixgill shark under the name "cow sharks", making it difficult to evaluate landings data. The shallow coastal nurseries in temperate zones probably make it vulnerable to overfishing.

4.2.3 Bramble sharks, Family Echinorhinidae

This is a small family consisting of only two species of rarely seen deep-water sharks.

Bramble shark (*Echinorhinus brucus*)

The bramble shark is a large squaloid shark widely distributed in deep temperate and tropical waters. It is a poorly known species usually found at depths of 350-900 m. It is often reported from the eastern Atlantic and the western Indian Ocean. Only three or four specimens have been reported from the North American East Coast in the last hundred years.

Reproductive potential: There is almost no information on its reproductive processes. A brood of 24 young has been reported, but it is likely that the average brood is much larger, based on egg-bearing females seen by the authors. The young probably reach 40 cm TL at birth. There are no data on the gestation period nor on the length of the reproductive cycle.

Impact of fisheries: According to Quero and Emonnet (1993), the shark was often seen as bycatch in trawl catches in the early nineteenth century off Rochebonne, France, but its numbers have been diminishing steadily. The species has virtually disappeared from the Bay of Biscay, since only three specimens have been seen in the last 25 years.

Status: Category 4. The local disappearance of the species presumably caused by being captured in trawls for decades suggests that the species may be very long-lived and slow-reproducing, and that trawl bycatch fisheries may be sufficient to prevent replacement of local exploited populations.

Prickly shark (*Echinorhinus cookei*)

The prickly shark inhabits tropical and temperate waters of the Pacific Ocean. Most specimens recorded were accidental trawl catches at depths of 75-90 m (Castro 1983).

Status: Not-exploited species.

4.2.4 Dogfish sharks, Family Squalidae

The dogfishes, also known as squaloid sharks, are a large and diverse group found in a wide range of habitats and depths. They are primarily small fishes of deep, cool waters, although a few reach gigantic size. The group includes the only polar sharks known. Many species are of no interest to fisheries.

Not-exploited species:

Hooktooth dogfish (*Aculeola nigra*)
Needle dogfish (*Centrophorus acus*)
Dumb gulper shark (*Centrophorus harrissoni*)
Mosaic gulper shark (*Centrophorus tessellatus*)
Granular dogfish (*Centroscyllium granulatum*)
Bareskin dogfish (*Centroscyllium kamoharai*)
Combtooth dogfish (*Centroscyllium nigrum*)
Ornate dogfish (*Centroscyllium ornatum*)
Whitefin dogfish (*Centroscyllium ritteri*)
Shortnose velvet dogfish (*Centroscymnus cryptacanthus*)
Largespine velvet dogfish (*Centroscymnus macracanthus*)
Roughskin dogfish (*Centroscymnus owstoni*)
Mandarin dogfish (*Cirrhigaleus barbifer*)
Rough longnose dogfish (*Deania histricosa*)
Arrowhead dogfish (*Deania profundorum*)
Longsnout dogfish (*Deania quadrispinosum*)
Shorttail lanternshark (*Etmopterus brachyurus*)

Lined lanternshark (*Etmopterus bullisi*)
Cylindrical lanternshark (*Etmopterus carteri*)[1]
Combtoothed lanternshark (*Etmopterus decacuspidatus*)
Broadbanded lanternshark (*Etmopterus gracilispinis*)
Caribbean lanternshark (*Etmopterus hillianus*)
Blackbelly lanternshark (*Etmopterus lucifer*)
Pygmy lanternshark (*Etmopterus perryi*)
Great lanternshark (*Etmopterus princeps*)
Lanternshark (*Etmopterus robinsi*)
Fringefin lanternshark (*Etmopterus schultzi*)
Thorny lanternshark (*Etmopterus sentosus*)
Brown lanternshark (*Etmopterus unicolor*)
Hawaiian lanternshark (*Etmopterus villosus*)
Green lanternshark (*Etmopterus virens*)
Taillight shark (*Euprotomicroides zantedeschia*)
Pygmy shark (*Euprotomicrus bispinatus*)
Longnose pygmy shark (*Heteroscymnoides marleyi*)
Cookiecutter shark (*Isistius brasiliensis*)
Largetooth cookiecutter shark (*Isistius plutodus*)
Sherwood dogfish (*Scymnodalatias sherwoodi*)
Velvet dogfish (*Scymnodon squamulosus*)
Pacific sleeper shark (*Somniosus pacificus*)
Roughskin spurdog (*Squalus asper*)
Blacktailed spurdog (*Squalus melanurus*)
Cyrano spurdog (*Squalus rancureli*)

Category 1:

Gulper shark (*Centrophorus granulosus*)
Lowfin gulper shark (*Centrophorus lusitanicus*)
Smallfin gulper shark (*Centrophorus moluccensis*)
Taiwan gulper shark (*Centrophorus niaukang*)
Leafscale gulper shark (*Centrophorus squamosus*)
Little gulper shark (*Centrophorus uyato*)
Black dogfish (*Centroscyllium fabricii*)
Portuguese dogfish (*Centroscymnus coelolepis*)
Longnose velvet dogfish (*Centroscymnus crepidater*)
Plunket shark (*Centroscymnus plunketi*)
Birdbeak dogfish (*Deania calcea*)
African lantershark (*Etmopterus polli*)
Smooth lanternshark (*Etmopterus pusillus*)
Velvet belly (*Etmopterus spinax*)
Smallmouth velvet dogfish (*Scymnodon obscurus*)
Knifetooth dogfish (*Scymnodon ringens*)

---

1 Species described by Springer and Burgess in 1985, not included in Compagno 1984.

Little sleeper shark (*Somniosus rostratus*)

Spined pygmy shark (*Squaliolus laticaudus*)

Longnose spurdog (*Squalus blainvillei*)

Cuban dogfish (*Squalus cubensis*)

Japanese spurdog (*Squalus japonicus*)

Shortnose spurdog (*Squalus megalops*)

Shortspine spurdog (*Squalus mitsukurii*)

New Zealand lanternshark (*Etmopterus granulosus = E. baxteri*)[2]

This is a large lanternshark (possibly the largest of the lanternsharks), found in the temperate waters of the Southern Hemisphere (Last and Stevens 1994). It is utilized for its liver oil in small quantities in New Zealand (Summers and Wong 1992).

Status: Category 1

Kitefin shark (*Dalatias licha*)

This is a small, deep-water shark widely distributed in warm-temperate and tropical waters of the outer continental and insular shelves. It is most common below 200 m, and it has been caught as deep as 1800 m (Compagno 1984). It is common along the eastern Atlantic and the east coast of southern Africa, but very rare along the eastern North American coast. In the Azores, it is mainly caught at depths of 150-200 m, the deepest record being 1000 m (Krefft and Tortonese 1973).

Reproductive potential: Males probably mature at 95 cm TL and females at 120 cm TL (Castro 1983). According to da Silva (1983), the smallest gravid female seen by him measured 140 cm TL. Da Silva (1988) reported that the young are born at about 42 cm TL after a gestation period of two years. Da Silva (1983) reported broods of 7-14 young. Azorean fishermen reported never having seen a small kitefin shark, thus the nursery areas must be in other areas not fished by them. Da Silva (1988) gave estimates of the von Bertalanffy growth parameters as: L_∞ = 127 cm, K= 0.198 year^{-1}, t_0= -1.949 years.

Impact of fisheries: The largest fisheries appear to be off the Azores and Japan. According to da Silva (1983), it is one of the two most important demersal species in the Azores, where it is fished around three of the islands: Pico, Faial, and San Miguel. In Pico, it is the most important species in the fishery. Traditionally, the kitefin fishery used to be an artisanal handline fishery, but in the early 1980s, larger net boats entered the fishery (da Silva 1983). Annual catch and effort data exists since 1972 (ICES 1995). Landings (Fig. 1) peaked in 1981 with 947 t and decreased ever since to 309 t in 1994. The decline was attributed to overexploitation of the resource and to market fluctuations of the liver oil price. CPUE for the artisanal fishery also declined steadily from 1977 to 1982 (Fig. 2). According to official statistics (da Silva 1983), the price for the kitefin shark fell sharply in 1980/81. Therefore, the reduction in effort in 1982 was probably market driven.

Status: Category 3. Da Silva (1983) calculated a MSY of 579 t for the kitefin shark in the Azores, and stated that it would be unwise to increase the catches beyond that level. The same author, da Silva (1987) revised his MSY for both sexes together to 933 t year^{-1}, close to the maximum landings observed in 1981.

---

2 Considered as two distinguished species in Compagno 1984 but synonymized by Tachikawa, Taniuci and Arai, 1989.

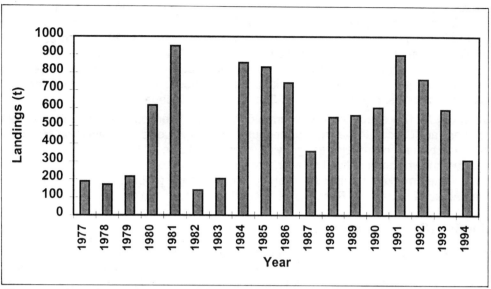

Figure 1. Landings of kitefin shark from the Azores (ICES Area X) (ICES 1995).

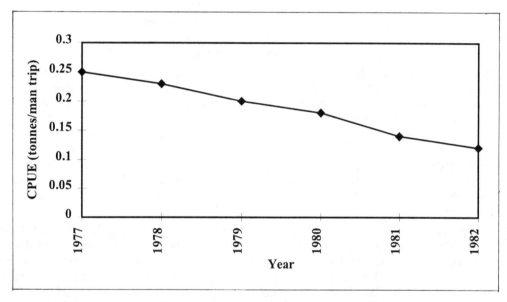

Figure 2. CPUE from 1977-1982 for the artisanal fishery for kitefin sharks around the islands of Faial and Pico, Azores (da Silva 1983).

Greenland shark (*Somniosus microcephalus*)

The Greenland shark is a very large squaloid shark of polar waters. It inhabits the North Atlantic Ocean from polar latitudes to the North Sea in the east and the Gulf of Saint Lawrence in the west. It is the only shark regularly found in polar waters where the temperature is 2-7^{0}C. It is a deep-water species that only comes to the surface during the cooler months. It reaches 640 cm TL and over 1 t. Its flesh is poisonous, and must be dried or boiled several times before it can be consumed, a fact that has probably inhibited its use for human consumption.

Reproductive potential: Almost nothing is known about its reproductive processes. The young are believed to measure about 38 cm TL at birth, based on the examination of a single near term foetus by Bjerkan and Koefoed (1957). Tagging studies have shown the Greenland shark to be a very slow-growing species (Hansen 1963), but there are no estimates of age at maturity or longevity.

Impact of fisheries: Norway had a commercial fishery for Greenland sharks for centuries. Most of the catch came from the Arctic region, where the fishery was often combined with sealing. The fishery in Greenland started in the very early nineteenth century. In 1857, the fishery was estimated at only

2 000-3 000 sharks annually, by the 1890s it had grown to 11 500-15 000 sharks, and in the 1910s it had grown to 32 000 sharks year[-1] (Jensen 1914). The commercial fishery for the Greenland shark ended in 1960, because the liver oil was no longer profitable (ICES 1995). In the early 1970, there was a subsidized fishery in western Norway to reduce the stock, because it had become a problem for other fisheries. A letter from the Norwegian Directorate for Nature Management to the senior author in September 1995 did not include the Greenland shark among the species fished for by Norway. Iceland has had a small fishery that averaged 38 t for the last decade.

Status: Category 3. The effects of the fisheries of the early twentieth century and the status of the Greenland shark are difficult to determine, because of the lack of data. Based on Hansen's (1963) studies, this may be one of the slowest-growing sharks and one of the longest-lived vertebrates on earth. Given the known reproductive limitations of sharks, it is probably a very fragile species, but its Arctic habitat, limited markets for its liver oil and poisonous flesh probably reduce fishery interest and afford some degree of protection. Research is needed to clarify its status.

Picked dogfish (*Squalus acanthias*)

The picked or spiny dogfish, a small coastal shark of the family Squalidae, is possibly the most abundant living shark and the only one that supports fisheries of a size rivalling those of the more commercially important bony fishes (Compagno 1984). It inhabits warm temperate to boreal waters throughout the world. It is a highly gregarious fish that forms very large, highly localized schools, usually composed of hundreds or thousands of sharks of uniform size or sex. These schools undertake north-south coastal migrations and onshore-offshore movements that are not fully understood. These migrations are controlled by temperature, as the picked dogfish prefers temperatures of 6-11^{0}C. It has been one of the most intensely studied fishes (Jensen 1966), because it is one of the relatively few sharks that can be kept in captivity for a few years.

Reproductive potential: According to Nammack *et al.* (1985), females mature at 80 cm TL and 12.1 years of age, and males mature at 60 cm TL and 6 years. Those authors estimated the maximum ages for males and females of the Northwest Atlantic to be 35 and 40 years of age, respectively, while Beamish and McFarlane (1985) estimated that off British Columbia, the species reaches at least 70 years of age. Beamish and McFarlane (1985) used the dogfish spine annuli to age them and validated their estimates with tagging and by the recovery of tetracycline-injected animals. The picked dogfish had the longest known gestation period of any vertebrate. Estimates range from 20-22 months (Hisaw and Albert 1947) to 21-25 months (Ford 1921). Broods consist of 3-11 young, which measure about 25 cm TL at birth (Jensen 1966). Off North America, the nurseries are believed to be in offshore waters in the southern part of the range (Castro 1983).

Impact of fisheries: In the northeastern Atlantic catches have declined (Fig. 3) from 40 384 t in 1985 to 16 109 t in 1996 (FAO 1996, 1998). In the western North Atlantic, catches of picked dogfish and those reported by USA as not identified Squalidae species, most of which are picked dogfish catches, increased from 4 066 t in 1985 to 27 757 in 1996 (Fig. 4), primarily as a result of the increases in US catches (FAO 1996, 1998). The United States catches were about 500 t annually in the 1960s, and remained at less than 1 000 t annually until the late 1970s. Landings increased to about 4 800 t in 1979 and remained fairly steady for the next ten years, averaging 4 500 t annually. Landings increased sharply (Fig. 5) to 14 870 t in 1990, dropped slightly in 1991, and increased to 17 160 t in 1992 and 20 360 t in 1993 (NEFSC 1994). This sharp increase was attributed to the decline of the more valuable groundfish stocks that forced fishermen to target other species. Additional quantities of picked dogfish are caught and discarded. It was estimated by NEFSC (1994) that an additional 13 500 t of dogfish were killed and discarded off the northeastern coast of North America, the total 1993 catch then being about 36 000 t. Data are lacking to estimate discards prior to 1993.

Status: Category 4. The vulnerability to overfishing of the picked dogfish has been known for a long time. Holden (1968), in his assessment of the effects of fishing upon the Norwegian-Scottish stocks of picked dogfish, wrote that the females "must be given considerable protection if recruitment is not to be affected". This has not been done in any of the current fisheries. Stock assessment of spiny dogfish resources of the northeastern coast of North America was carried out in the United States in 1994 at the 18th Northeast Regional Stock Assessment Workshop (NEFSC 1994). This group estimated that at current fishing mortality (F=0.26) would result in "negative replacement" and that under those conditions, stocks would eventually decline. The same group suggested that a management programme should be instituted quickly for the picked dogfish and appropriate management targets for biomass and fishing mortality should be established. That group also stated that all the evidence indicated the existence of a single stock of picked dogfish in the Northwest Atlantic and that joint management of the stock by the USA and Canada should be considered.

We consider the picked dogfish to be Category 4 because of its longevity, long gestation cycle, and the historical trends of dogfish catches. Northeastern Atlantic catches have declined by about 50% since 1985, based on FAO (1996, 1998) statistics. The stock of the northwestern Atlantic is considered already fully utilized and has possibly begun to decline as a consequence of the recent increase in exploitation and the concentration of the fishery on mature females, based on the 1994 stock assessment (NEFSC 1994).

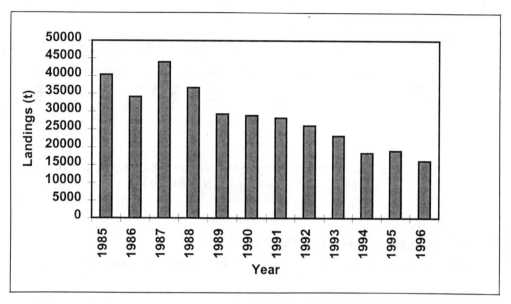

Figure 3. Picked dogfish landings for FAO Area 27 (FAO 1996, 1998).

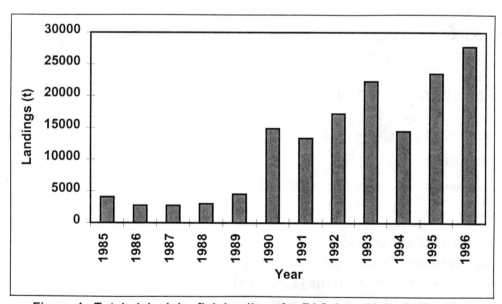

Figure 4. Total picked dogfish landings for FAO Area 21, including USA landings (FAO 1996, 1998).

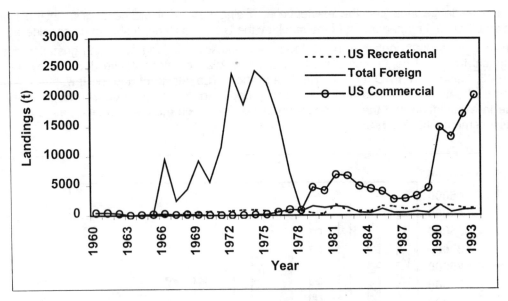

Figure 5. Picked dogfish landings from NAFO sub-areas 2-6 by the United States and other countries (NEFSC 1994).

4.2.5 Rough sharks, Family Oxynotidae

This is a small family of four species of deep-water sharks, occasionally caught in trawls.

Not-exploited:

Prickly dogfish (*Oxynotus bruniensis*)
Caribbean roughshark (*Oxynotus caribbaeus*)

Category 1:

Angular roughshark (*Oxynotus centrina*)
Sailfin roughshark (*Oxynotus paradoxus*)

4.2.6 Sawsharks, Family Pristiophoridae

The sawsharks are a small family of primarily deep-water species characterized by having the snout flattened into a blade with teeth on its sides.

Not-exploited:

Bahamas sawshark (*Pristiophorus schroederi*)

Category 1:

Sixgill sawshark (*Pliotrema warreni*)
Longnose sawshark (*Pristiophorus cirratus*)
Japanese sawshark (*Pristiophorus japonicus*)
Shortnose sawshark (*Pristiophorus nudipinnis*)

4.2.7 Angel sharks, Family Squatinidae

The angel sharks are flattened, ray-like, sharks of shallow coastal waters in tropical and warm temperate areas.

Not-exploited:

Sand devil (*Squatina dumeril*)

Taiwan angel shark (*Squatina formosa*)

Ornate angel shark (*Squatina tergocellata*)

Ocellated angel shark (*Squatina tergocellatoides*)

Category 1:

Sawback angel shark (*Squatina aculeata*)

African angel shark (*Squatina africana*)

Argentine angel shark (*Squatina argentina*)

Australian angel shark (*Squatina australis*)

Japanese angel shark (*Squatina japonica*)

Clouded angel shark (*Squatina nebulosa*)

Smoothback angel shark (*Squatina oculata*)

Angel shark (*Squatina squatina*)

Pacific angel shark (*Squatina californica*)

This is a common angel shark of warm-temperate, littoral bottom shark of the Pacific coast of North and South America (Compagno 1984). There is a localized gillnet fishery for the species off California, in the west coast of the United States (Cailliet *et al.* 1991).

Reproductive potential: According to Natanson and Cailliet (1986) both males and females reach sexual maturity at 90-100 cm TL, and reproduction is annual, and the average brood consists of six young. Age at maturity is uncertain because in this species the vertebral bands are not deposited annually, their formation being related to somatic growth (Natanson and Cailliet 1990). Cailliet *et al.* (1992) performed a demographic analysis of the species, which yielded a net reproductive rate (R_0) of 2.25, and a generation time of 14.5 years.

Impact of fisheries: A localized bottom gillnet fishery operated for a number of years off California, where the species went from "trash fish" status to one of California's most highly sought after commercial species in about ten years (Richards 1987). In 1985, the pacific angel shark replaced the thresher shark as the principal food shark from southern California. Landings in this fishery (Fig. 6) peaked in 1985 and 1986 at 562 and 564 t respectively (Cailliet *et al.* 1991), but declined rapidly afterwards. The decline was the result of a combination of declining availability and alternative sources of low-cost imported shark meat (Cailliet *et al.* 1991).

Cailliet *et al.* (1992) stated that off California, the pacific angel sharks enter the fishery at the same age and size at which they first reproduce. After a comprehensive analysis, these authors recommended that, until accurate estimates of mortality become available, it would be prudent to set a size limit considerably above the size at first reproduction, to protect the Pacific angel shark in California. The California fishery was largely ended by law in 1993 (D. Holts pers. comm.). Some restricted fishing is allowed to continue, but the fishery is thought to be very small now.

Status: Category 3. Based on the California experience, we classify the species as category 3, based on its long generation time, and the fact that the species enters the fishery at the same size it matures.

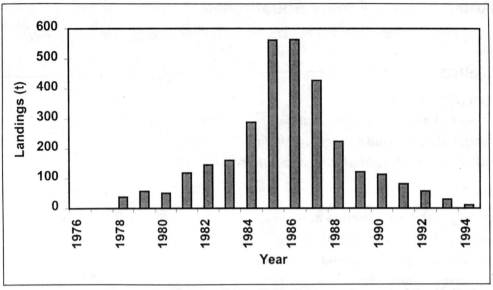

Figure 6. Pacific angel shark landings 1976-1994, west coast of the United States (Cailliet *et al.* 1991, Holts unpublished ms.).

4.2.8 Bullhead sharks, Family Heterodontidae

The bullhead sharks, also known as Port Jackson sharks are small, sluggish sharks that inhabit shallow warm waters throughout the world. They are of little or no interest to fisheries, although they are sometimes found in bycatch.

Category 1:

Horn shark (*Heterodontus francisci*)

Crested bullhead shark (*Heterodontus galeatus*)

Japanese bullhead shark (*Heterodontus japonicus*)

Mexican hornshark (*Heterodontus mexicanus*)

Port Jackson shark (*Heterodontus portusjacksoni*)

Galapagos bullhead shark (*Heterodontus quoyi*)

Whitespotted bullhead shark (*Heterodontus ramalheira*)

Zebra bullhead shark (*Heterodontus zebra*)

4.2.9 Collared carpetsharks, Family Parascyllidae

The collared carpetsharks are bottom dwelling sharks in temperate to tropical waters. They are found in the western Pacific, Australia to Japan (Compagno 1984). The maximum size is less than a metre.

Not-exploited:

Barbelthroat carpetshark (*Cirrhoscyllium expolitum*)

Taiwan saddled carpetshark (*Cirrhoscyllium formosanum*)

Saddle carpetshark (*Cirrhoscyllium japonicum*)

Collared carpetshark (*Parascyllium collare*)

Rusty carpetshark (*Parascyllium ferrugineum*)

Tasmanian carpetshark (*Parascyllium multimaculatum*)

Necklace carpetshark (*Parascyllium variolatum*)

4.2.10 Blind sharks, Family Brachaeluridae

The blind sharks are inshore bottom dwelling sharks of northern and southern Australia. They are small and commonly found on rocky bottoms or inshore coral reefs.

Not-exploited:

Blind shark (*Brachaelurus waddi*)
Bluegray carpetshark (*Heteroscyllium colcloughi*)

4.2.11 Wobbegongs, Family Orectolobidae

The wobbegongs are common bottom sharks with cryptic coloration that can be found in rocky areas or coral reefs throughout the temperate and tropical waters of the western Pacific Ocean.

Not-exploited:

Tasselled wobbegong (*Eucrossorhinus dasypogon*)
Northern wobbegong (*Orectolobus wardi*)
Cobbler wobbegong (*Sutorectus tentaculatus*)

Category 1:

Japanese wobbegong (*Orectolobus japonicus*)
Spotted wobbegong (*Orectolobus maculatus*)
Ornate wobbegong (*Orectolobus ornatus*)

4.2.12 Bamboo sharks, Family Hemiscylliidae

The bamboo sharks are hardy, small, inshore bottom dwelling animals. They are found in the western Pacific, from Madagascar to Japan, the Philippines and eastern Australia. They inhabit rocky bottoms, coral reefs, and tide-pools. They have the ability to use their fins in a leg-like manner (Compagno 1984).

Not-exploited:

Arabian carpetshark (*Chiloscyllium arabicum*)
Indonesian speckled carpetshark (*Hemiscyllium freycineti*)
Papuan epaulette shark (*Hemiscyllium hallstromi*)
Epaulette shark (*Hemiscyllium ocellatum*)
Hooded carpetsharks (*Hemiscyllium strahani*)
Speckled carpetshark (*Hemiscyllium trispeculare*)

Category 1:

Bluespotted bambooshark (*Chiloscyllium caerulopunctatum*)
Grey bambooshark (*Chiloscyllium griseum*)
Slender bambooshark (*Chiloscyllium indicum*)
Whitespotted bambooshark (*Chiloscyllium plagiosum*)
Brownbanded bambooshark (*Chiloscyllium punctatum*)

4.2.13   Zebra sharks, Family Stegostomatidae

Zebra shark (Stegostoma fasciatum)

The Zebra shark is a common shark with a wide range in the Indo-West Pacific, from South Africa to the Red Sea, the waters off India, China and Australia. It is a tropical inshore shark common to coral reefs. It is the only species in this family.

Status: Category 1.

4.2.14   Nurse sharks, Family Ginglymostomatidae

This family of sharks are bottom feeders that are distributed throughout the tropical and subtropical areas. They range from inshore waters to at least 70 m depth (Compagno 1984).

Category 1:

Short-tail nurse shark (Ginglymostoma brevicaudatum)

Tawny nurse shark (Nebrius ferrugineus)

Nurse shark (Ginglymostoma cirratum)

The nurse shark inhabits littoral waters on both sides of the tropical and subtropical Atlantic, ranging through tropical West Africa and the Cape Verde Islands in the east, and from North Carolina, USA to Brazil in the west; and in the eastern Pacific from the Gulf of California to Panama and Ecuador (Bigelow and Schroeder 1948). It is a shallow water species, often found lying motionless on the bottom under coral reefs or rocks. Often, it congregates in large numbers in shallow water (Castro 1983).

Reproductive potential: The nurse shark matures at about 225 cm TL (Springer 1938). The young measure about 30 cm TL at birth and broods consist of 20-30 young. The gestation period is about five to six months and it reproduces biennially (Castro unpublished data). The age at maturity is unknown, but it is a long-lived species. Clark (1963) reported an aquarium specimen living up to 24 years in captivity. Its nurseries are in shallow turtle grass beds and coral reefs (Castro unpublished data).

Impact of fisheries: In North America and the Caribbean, the nurse shark has often been pursued for its hide. Its hide is said to be more valuable than that of any other shark (Springer 1950a). The fins have no value and the value of the meat is questionable (Springer 1979). In North America, where it is not utilized for its hide, it is often considered a nuisance and killed by fishermen (Castro pers. obs.).

Status: Category 1. We have little data on nurse shark landings anywhere in its range.

4.2.15   Whale shark, Family Rhincodontidae

Whale shark (Rhincodon typus)

The whale shark is a huge, sluggish, pelagic filter-feeder, often seen swimming on the surface. It is the largest fish in the oceans, reaching lengths of 1 210 cm TL and perhaps larger. It is found throughout all tropical seas, usually far offshore (Castro 1983).

Reproductive potential: Recent discoveries prove the whale shark to be viviparous and the most prolific of all sharks (Joung et al. 1996). The only gravid female examined carried 300 young in several stages of development. The embryos measured 58-64 cm TL, the largest appearing ready for birth. The length of the reproductive cycle is unknown. It is probably biennial like the closely related nurse shark (Ginglymostoma cirratum) and most other large sharks (Castro 1996). There are no data on age and growth of the species, but based on unpublished information on the growth rate of one of surviving embryos from the female reported by Joung et al. (1996), the whale shark may prove to be the fastest growing shark. Only a handful of small juveniles has ever been caught, probably because of the extremely fast growth rate. The location of the whale shark nurseries is unknown and remains one of the interesting mysteries of shark biology.

Impact of fisheries: There have been a few small fisheries in India, the Philippines, and Taiwan, but it is of little commercial importance elsewhere. The whale shark used to be fished for its flesh, but presently the fins and oil are also used. According to Ramachandran and Sankar (1990), no organized fishery exists in India, except in Veraval where fishing is conducted for a short period during February-May exclusively for the oil. According to Silas (1986), a small harpoon fishery occurs in certain years, when whale sharks are abundant in Gujarat waters in northwest India. This fishery took about 40 whale sharks in 1982, of which 22 were taken to Veraval for liver removal during 12-15 April 1982. Silas (1986) stated that captures were sporadic or even fortuitous. According to Joung *et al.* (1996), fishermen in the southern coast of Taiwan used to catch 30-100 whale sharks in a season. By the late 1980s, less than 10 sharks were being caught per season. According to Joung *et al.* (1996), Taiwanese fishermen in An-Ping Harbor caught more than 70 whale sharks in 1992, only 2 in 1993, and 14 in 1994. The fishery in the Philippines is poorly known. The fishery appears to be centered in the Bohol Sea, according to an unpublished report by the WWF-Philippines Program (Trono 1996). According to this source, fishermen in Talisayan (one of the four sites visited in the Bohol Sea) reported catching 100 sharks in 1994, 80 sharks in 1995 and only 30 for the 1996 season. Based on interviews with the fishermen from the four sites, 95 sharks were landed during the 1996 season.

Status: Category 2. The size of the whale shark generally safeguards it from most fisheries. The only fisheries targeting the whale shark are very small and it is difficult to evaluate what impact, if any, they have on the populations. However, records of the Taiwanese fishery suggest that whale sharks, like most elasmobranchs, are susceptible to overfishing. The whale shark is one of the species used by the conservation movement as a symbol for threatened sharks, in spite of the lack of data on populations or the effects of the present level of fishing on the entire population.

4.2.16 Sand tiger sharks, Family Odontaspididae

These are tropical to temperate, inshore to deep-water sharks. There are only four species in the family. Most of the species are poorly known, except for the sand tiger shark.

Not-exploited:

Smalltooth sand tiger (*Odontaspis ferox*)

Bigeye sand tiger (*Odontaspis noronhai*)

Category 1:

Indian sand tiger (*Eugomphodus tricuspidatus*)

Sand tiger shark (*Carcharias taurus*)

The sand tiger shark, also known as grey nurse shark, is a large, sluggish shallow water predator found in temperate waters throughout the world. It is often found in very shallow water (<4 m) (Castro 1983). It is the most popular large shark in aquaria, because it survives easily in captivity, unlike most other sharks. It is fished for its flesh and fins in coastal longline fisheries.

Reproductive potential: Gilmore *et al.* (1983) stated that sand tiger males off the eastern coast of the United States mature at 192 cm TL. According to Branstetter and Musick (1994), males in that area reach maturity at 190-195 cm TL or 4-5 years, and females mature at more than 220 cm TL or 6 years. The largest immature female seen off the United States by the senior author (Castro) was 225 cm TL and the smallest gravid female was 229 cm TL, suggesting that maturity is reached at 225-229 cm TL. The oldest fish in Branstetter and Musick's (1994) sample of 55 sharks was 10.5 years old, an age that has been exceeded in captivity (Govender *et al.* 1991). The von Bertalanffy parameters according to Branstetter and Musick (1994) are for males: L_∞= 301 cm, K= 0.17 year^{-1}, t_0= -2.25 years; and for females: L_∞= 323, K= 0.14, t_0= -2.56. The ageing has not been validated. The sand tiger has an extremely limited reproductive potential, producing only two young per brood (Springer 1948). In North America, the sand tiger gives birth in March and April to two young that measure about 100 cm TL. The nursery areas are not well defined, it appears to give birth over a wide area. Branstetter and Musick (1994) suggested that the reproductive cycle is biennial, but this needs to be verified.

Impact of fisheries: It is very vulnerable to fisheries, because it congregates in large numbers, probably for mating, at particular coastal spots at specific times of the year. These spots are known to commercial fishermen who can catch very large numbers of sand tigers with minimal effort, but with serious effects on the population. According to Pollard (1996), it was one of the first sharks to receive fully protected status anywhere in the world, achieving that status in New South Wales, Australia, in 1984, out of concerns of severe population declines that started in the 1960s and 1970s. Part of the population decline was attributed to divers who hunted them with powerheads (explosive devices) for sport. According to Stevens (1993), the numbers of sand tiger sharks caught in the South Wales beach netting decreased from an average of 30 year^{-1} in the 1951-1954 period to 1-2 year^{-1} for the 1988-1990 period, to 0 in 1993. In the United States, there was a very severe population decline in the early 1990s, with sand tigers practically disappearing from North Carolina and Florida waters (R. Grant Gilmore, Harbor Branch Foundation, pers. comm.). Musick *et al.* (1993) documented a decrease in the Chesapeake Bight region of the US Mid-Atlantic coast in CPUE of 1 shark /100 hooks average in the 1974-1979 period to 0.2 sharks /100 hooks in 1991. In April 1997, the United States prohibited all directed (commercial and recreational) fishing for the sand tiger on the Atlantic coast.

Status: Category 4. The species has become rare in Australia (Pollard 1996) and along the coast of the United States (Gilmore pers. comm.). The species is vulnerable to overfishing, because it congregates in coastal areas in very large numbers during the mating season. These aggregations are very attractive to fishermen who can deplete a local population in a short time. Its very limited fecundity (two young per brood) probably contributes to its vulnerability.

4.2.17 Goblin sharks, Family Mitsukurinidae

Goblin shark (*Mitsukurina owstoni*)

The goblin shark is the only member of this family. It is one of the deepest dwelling species of sharks, and thus it is very seldom encountered anywhere, except for Japan, where most of the specimens examined have originated.

Status: Not-exploited.

4.2.18 Crocodile sharks, Family Pseudocarchariidae

Crocodile shark (*Pseudocarcharias kamoharai*)

The crocodile shark is the only member of this family. It is a tropical species often caught on tuna longlines.

Status: Category 1.

4.2.19 Megamouth sharks, Family Megachasmidae

Megamouth shark (*Megachasma pelagios*)

The only member of this family is the megamouth shark, a very large deep-water shark that was not described until 1983. Little is known about it.

Status: Not-exploited.

4.2.20 Thresher sharks, Family Alopiidae

These are large primarily oceanic sharks with tremendously elongated tails. There are three species in the family.

Pelagic thresher (*Alopias pelagicus*)

The pelagic thresher is a poorly known oceanic shark of the Pacific and Indian Oceans. It appears to be a smaller species than the other two threshers. It is often confused with *Alopias vulpinus*.

Reproductive potential: The embryos of the pelagic thresher have been shown to be oophagous and only two young are produced in each brood (Otake and Mizue 1981). The lengths of the reproductive cycle and gestation period are unknown.

Impact of fisheries: Pelagic threshers are caught in tuna and swordfish longlines (Hanan *et al.* 1993, Compagno 1984, Otake and Mizue 1981), but many are misidentified as common threshers. The only data available are for the southern California (USA) fishery from 1981 to 1991.

Status: Category 3. The pelagic thresher has a very limited reproductive potential, even more limited than the common thresher, so the effect of fisheries on the pelagic thresher is probably more severe. The small California fishery most likely exemplifies the inability of the species to support intensive exploitation.

Bigeye thresher (*Alopias superciliosus*)

The bigeye thresher is cosmopolitan in warm and warm-temperate waters. It is a deep-water species that ascends to depths of 35-150 m at night. It feeds on squid and small schooling fishes (Castro 1983), which it stuns with blows from its tail. This is one of the larger sharks, reaching up to 460 cm TL (Nakamura 1935).

Reproductive potential: According to Moreno and Morón (1992) eastern Atlantic males mature at about 270 cm TL and females at about 340 cm TL. According to Chen *et al.* (1997) males in the northwestern pacific mature at 270-288 cm TL and females at 332-341 cm TL. Liu *et al.* (1998) gave the ages at maturity for northwestern pacific bigeye threshers as 9-10 years for males and 12.3-13.4 years for females; their largest female being was 20 years old while the largest male was 19 years old. Liu *et al.* (1998) gave the von Bertalanffy parameters as L_∞=224.6 cm, K=0.092 year^{-1}, t_0=-4.21 years for females; and L_∞=218.8, K=0.088, and t_0=-4.24 for males, giving a maximum size less than some reported sizes at first maturity. Broods consist of two young, one in each uterus, that measure 135-140 cm TL at birth (Chen *et al.* 1997). According to Chen *et al.* (1997) there is no fixed mating or birth season in the northwestern Pacific. Gestation probably lasts about a year, but there is no direct evidence to support this. The length of the reproductive cycle is unknown.

Impact of fisheries: The bigeye thresher is most often seen in the bycatch of swordfish fisheries, where it is considered a nuisance. A shark will often dislodge several baits before impaling or hooking itself. The flesh and fins of the bigeye thresher are of poor quality, thus it is usually discarded dead in swordfish and tuna fisheries. However, it is marketed in some areas, but landings statistics are very scarce. Sri Lanka reported landings 981 t (data submitted to FAO by Sri Lanka in 1996). Liu *et al.* (1998) reported that the bigeye thresher constituted 13% of the annual shark catch at the Nan Fan Ao fish market in Taiwan.

Status: Category 3. It is difficult to evaluate the status of the bigeye thresher because the lack of fisheries data. However, its slow growth, limited reproductive potential, and the fact that it is caught in large numbers in numerous tuna and swordfish fisheries throughout its range (Gubanov 1978, Compagno 1984, Berkeley and Campos 1988, etc.) warrant placing it in Category 3.

Thresher shark (*Alopias vulpinus*)

The thresher shark is cosmopolitan in warm and temperate waters. It is found in both coastal and oceanic waters, but according to Strasburg (1958) it is more abundant near land. It is a large shark that uses its tremendously large tail to hit and stun the small schooling fishes upon which it feeds.

Reproductive potential: According to Strasburg (1958), females in the Pacific mature at about 315 cm TL. According to Cailliet and Bedford (1983), males mature at about 333 cm TL. Cailliet and Bedford (1983) stated that the age at maturity ranges from 3 to 7 years. Broods consist of 4 to 6 young, which measure 137-155 cm TL at birth (Castro 1983). According to Bedford (1985), gestation lasts 9 months and female threshers give birth annually every spring (March to June).

Impact of fisheries: Thresher sharks are caught in many fisheries, but data on catches or landings are scarce. Thresher sharks are often caught incidentally by longline vessels, which target tunas, marlins and swordfish, but there is no published data known to the authors on thresher landings in those fisheries. Many of the thresher sharks caught in California gill net fisheries have longline hooks embedded in their mouths, indicating encounters with longline fisheries (Hanan 1984). The most detailed data available to the authors are for the California drift gill net fishery which started in 1977 for thresher sharks, shortfin makos, and swordfish, extending from the Mexican border to San Francisco, California (Hanan 1984). Market demand grew quickly, and the fishery was further stimulated by the more valuable catch of swordfish (Cailliet and Bedford 1983, Holts 1988). Swordfish became the primary target species and the number of vessels grew to over 200 by 1982. Despite of several attempts to limit the fishery, it grew and expanded for several years. After 1982, the fishery expanded northward yearly, ultimately reaching the states of Oregon and Washington (Cailliet *et al.* 1991). Thresher shark landings peaked in 1982 at 1 087 t (Fig. 7), and the thresher shark resource quickly began to decline after that year (Bedford 1987). Catches have continued to decline and the average size has remained small in spite of numerous regulations restricting fishing (Hanan *et al.*

24

1993). Cailliet *et al.* (1991) summarized the condition of the resource by stating, "The coastwise fishery for this once abundant shark is now a thing of the past." Legislation passed in 1986 limited the directed thresher shark fishery to 30 days in the month of May. Approximately 50% of the annual catch was taken during this period, while the remainder was taken as bycatch in the swordfish fishery during the fall and winter months. Landings in the fishery remain steady at about 273 t year^{-1}, consisting of one to two years old, immature fish (Cailliet *et al.* 1991). Off the US coast in the Atlantic Ocean, the CPUE has shown a considerable decline 1980-1994 (Fig. 8).

Status: Category 4. The thresher is rated Category 4, because it has a low reproductive potential and it is the target of many intensive fisheries throughout the world.

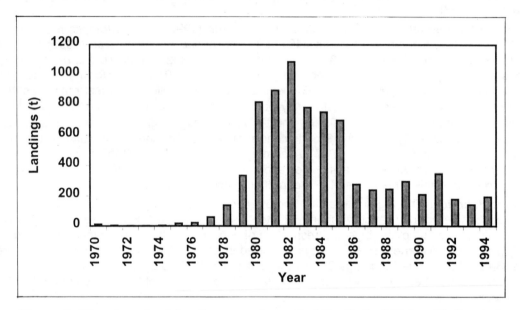

Figure 7. Thresher shark landings, west coast of the United States (Holts *et al.* 1996).

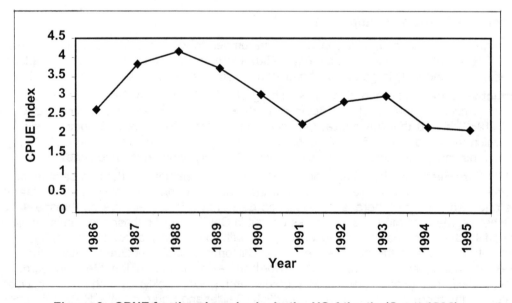

Figure 8. CPUE for thresher sharks in the US Atlantic (Scott 1996).

4.2.21 Basking sharks, Family Cetorhinidae

The basking shark is the sole member of this family.

Basking shark (*Cetorhinus maximus*)

The basking shark is the second largest fish in the world, its size exceed only by the whale shark. Like the whale shark, it is a filter-feeder. It is a migratory species of the sub-polar and cold temperate seas throughout the world. It spends the summer in high latitudes, moving into warmer water in winter (Castro 1983). In spite of its size and local abundance in summer, its habits are very poorly known. During the European autumn, basking sharks disappear and are not seen until the following summer, when they return after giving birth.

Reproductive potential: Almost nothing is known about its reproductive processes. Males are believed to reach maturity between 460 and 610 cm (Bigelow and Schroeder 1948) and an estimated age of 4-5 years (Parker and Stott 1965). Females mature at 810-980 cm (Compagno 1984). It is believed to give birth to young measuring about 180 cm TL, probably in high latitudes. There are no modern reports on the brood size and no data on reproductive cycles.

Impact of fisheries: There have been fisheries for the basking shark in northern Europe since the earliest times, when its liver oil was used for lamp oil. In the mid-twentieth century, it was fished around the British Isles for its liver oil as a source of vitamin A. From 1947 to 1975, basking sharks were netted and harpooned around Achill Island off of the west coast of Ireland, at one point catching well over a thousand sharks annually (ICES 1995). Parker and Stott (1965) described this fishery during the 1950s and attributed its decline to overfishing. In the 1960s and 1970s, more than 30 vessels participated in the European fishery for the whole or part of the season (ICES 1995). Today, it is fished for its fins, primarily in a Norwegian fishery of only a few boats (Fig. 9). Norwegian fin exports to Japan have been steadily increasing: 0.096 t of fins were exported in 1992; 7.218 t in 1993; and 26.859 t in 1994 (Letter from Directorate for Nature Management, 21 Sep 1995). Kunzlik (1988) gave an excellent summary of the present knowledge on the basking shark. In contrast to the opinions of others, Kunzlik attributed the decline of the basking shark fisheries to the erratic nature of their seasonal appearances and to the collapse in the price paid for their livers, and stated that "there is no firm evidence to suggest that the species has been threatened, even locally, by exploitation". Sims *et al.* (1997) and Sims and Quayle (1998) have shown that basking sharks forage along thermal fronts and seek the highest densities of zooplankton, demonstrating that the appearance of basking sharks is directly related to zooplankton abundance.

A sporadic fishery for basking sharks existed off central California (USA) earlier this century. Clark (1887) reporting on whaling activities off Monterey, California, stated that in 1880 two sharks had been obtained, and that "the basking shark is rare here, sometimes not seen for 20 years". By the early part of the century, the basking shark was reported as abundant off central California. Chute (1930) noted that fishermen in Monterey Bay had reported sightings of up to 500 sharks at time. Walford (1935) stated that basking sharks appeared in schools of 20-30 individuals in Monterey and San Simeon Bays during the winter months. Roedel and Ripley (1950) stated that schools of 75-100 individuals had been seen.

A basking shark harpoon fishery first developed in California in 1924. Between 1924 and 1938, the yearly average was 25 sharks, but in one year 100 sharks were taken (Phillips 1948). In the late 1940s, the fishery expanded using war surplus aircraft and amphibious vehicles (Fitch 1948). Between September 1946 and May 1947, about 300 basking sharks were taken along the California coast (Phillips 1948). Fishing for basking sharks was suspended in California in October 1950, because the low prices paid for the oil and the low availability of basking sharks (Squire 1967).

In the 1950s, a basking shark culling programme was conducted in British Columbia waters by the Canadian Fisheries Department, because basking sharks were damaging salmon nets. About 50 sharks were reported killed in the first month of operation (Squire 1990).

From 1962 to 1985, the National Marine Fisheries Service, Southwest Fisheries Science Center conducted an aerial monitoring programme for pelagic fishes, using a spotter aircraft working with the California purse seine fleet. A total of 399 sightings totalling 8 709 basking sharks were recorded (Squire 1990). Greater abundances were observed prior to 1970. Fluctuations in abundance were attributed to abnormally warm years and El Niño perturbations.

Status: Category 3. Catches in the EEC waters are limited to 400 t of liver weight, but there is now concern for the stocks (Muñoz-Chapuli *et al.* 1993). According to the ICES Study Group on Elasmobranch Fishes (ICES 1995), there is a lack of biological knowledge on basking sharks, on age structure and stock identity, and it is unlikely that assessments of population size or mortality rates can be carried out with the available data. The basking shark fisheries of the past suggest that the species is vulnerable to overfishing.

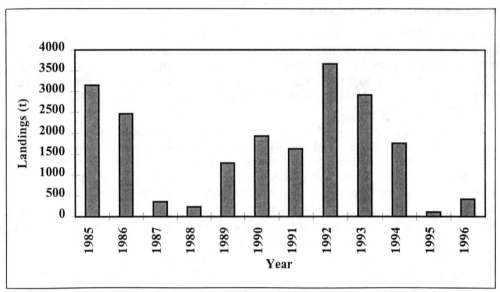

Figure 9. Norwegian and Portuguese basking shark landings in FAO Area 27 (FAO 1996, 1998).

4.2.22 Mackerel sharks, Family Lamnidae

This is a family consisting of five large, very active, widely distributed species.

Great white shark (*Carcharodon carcharias*)

The great white shark is the largest of the lamnid or mackerel sharks. It is a poorly known apex predator found throughout temperate, subtropical and tropical waters. It is at the top of the food chain, and thus its presence is always sporadic and nowhere can it be considered common (Castro 1983). Springer (1963) stated that in the Florida shark fishery of the 1940s, only 27 great white sharks in 100 000 sharks of all species were recorded over a period of 10 years. Large adults prey on seals and sealions, and sometimes found around their rookeries. It is also a scavenger of large dead whales. It has been described as the most voracious of the fish-like vertebrates and has been known to attack bathers, divers, and even boats.

Reproductive potential: Very little is known of its reproductive processes, because only two gravid females have been examined by biologists in modern times. Both specimens contained seven embryos. Recent observations show that great white sharks carry 7-10 embryos that are born at 120-150 cm TL (Uchida *et al.* 1996, Francis 1996). The lengths of the reproductive and gestation cycles are unknown. Great white sharks are believed to mature between 3.7 and 4.3 m at an estimated age of 9-10 years (Cailliet *et al.* 1985). Cailliet *et al.* (1985) estimated growth rates of 25-30 cm year^{-1} for juveniles and 21.8 cm year^{-1} for older specimens, and gave the following von Bertalanffy parameters: n= 21, L_∞= 763.7 cm, K= 0.058 year^{-1}, t_0= -3.53 years. They estimated that a 610 cm TL specimen would be 13-14 year old. The type of habitat and location of the nursery areas are unknown. It is likely that the nurseries will be found in the warmer parts of the range in deep water.

Impact of fisheries: It is a prized gamefish, because of its size. It is occasionally caught on commercial longlines or near-shore gillnets. Its jaws and teeth are often seen in specialized markets where they bring high prices. Preliminary observations (Strong *et al.* 1992) show that populations may be small and highly localized and very vulnerable to overexploitation.

Status: Category 3. The great white shark has been adopted as a symbol of a threatened species by some conservation organizations. The species has received protected status in South Africa and it has been added to Australian Threatened Fishes List in the "uncertain status" category. In 1997, the Unites States also prohibited all directed (commercial and recreational) fishing for the great white shark. However, the authors of this report have not found any population assessments or even anecdotal or published reports of any population decreases to justify placing the great white shark in any category higher than category 3. It is placed in this category, because it is a scarce apex predator, a long-lived species, has a limited reproductive potential, and is vulnerable to being caught in shark longlines.

Shortfin mako (*Isurus oxyrinchus*)

The shortfin mako is found in warm and warm-temperate waters throughout all oceans. It is an oceanic species at the top of the food chain, feeding on fast-moving fishes such as swordfish, tunas, and other sharks (Castro 1983). It is considered one of the great gamefish of the world and its flesh is rated as one of the best eating.

Reproductive potential: According to Pratt and Casey (1983), females mature at about 7 years of age. Cailliet *et al.* (1983) estimated the von Bertalanffy parameters for the shortfin as: L_∞= 321 cm, K= 0.072 year^{-1}, t_0= -3.75 years (from 44 observations). The gestation period is believed to last one year. The length of the reproductive cycle is unknown; like in most large sharks, it is probably biennial. The broods range from 12 to 20, although only a handful of broods have been examined (Castro unpublished data). There is circumstantial evidence that the nursery areas are in deep tropical waters. The life span of the species has been estimated at 11.5 years (Pratt and Casey 1983).

Impact of fisheries: The shortfin mako is a common bycatch in tuna and swordfish fisheries. In some of the pelagic fleets that have a large shark bycatch, shortfin mako carcasses are usually the only shark carcasses that are retained, because they bring a high market price (the other species are usually finned and their carcasses are discarded at sea). Off the northeastern coast of North America, most of the catch consists of immature fish (Casey and Kohler 1992). The index of abundance for shortfin makos in the commercial longline fishery off the Atlantic coast of the United States shows a steady decline from a catch index of 11.86 in 1986 to 3.52 in 1995 (Cramer 1996a). The landings of shortfin makos as bycatch from the swordfish fishery by the Azorean fleet in ICES Area X also shows a decrease from 14 and 11 t in 1987 and 1988 respectively, to 6 and 8 t in 1993 in 1994, respectively. On the eastern Pacific, shortfin mako landings have declined significantly 1987-1994 (Fig. 10) in landings (Holts *et al.* 1996).

Status: Category 4. It is very difficult to assess the status of the shortfin mako, because it is caught in so many different fisheries throughout the world. The few indices available all indicate substantial population decreases. Because the species is a common bycatch fish in swordfish and tuna operations which are so widely spread, it is reasonable to assume that similar decreases are occurring in those areas for which we have no data.

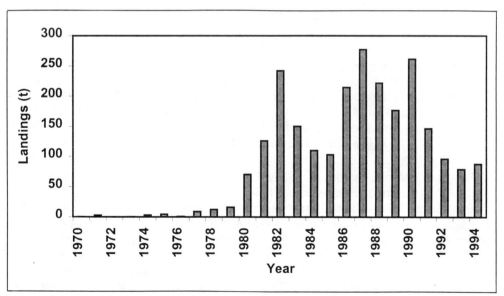

Figure 10. Shortfin mako landings off the west coast of the Unites States (Holts, *et al.* 1996).

Longfin mako (*Isurus paucus*)

This is a deep dwelling lamnid shark found in warm waters. The species was not described until 1966 and it is very poorly known, in spite of being a regular catch in pelagic fisheries.

Reproductive potential: There are few data on the reproductive processes of the longfin mako. Broods consist of 2-8 young that may reach 120 cm TL at birth (Castro unpublished data).

Impact of fisheries: The longfin mako is a seasonal bycatch of the pelagic tuna and swordfish fisheries. Unlike its congener the shortfin mako, its flesh is of lesser quality. Thus, it is often discarded at sea. Catch statistics reported to FAO by United States ranged from 2 to 12 t in the 1989-1994 years. These landings do not truly reflect the numbers of longfin mako that are discarded, because of poor markets for the species.

Status: Category 3. The species is considered Category 3, because of its low fecundity and its common appearance in swordfish lines.

Salmon shark (*Lamna ditropis*)

The geographical distribution of this lamnid species is limited to the North Pacific Ocean. It is a pelagic species of sub-arctic and cold temperate waters, a fast-moving predator at the top of the food chain (Castro 1983). It is morphologically and ecologically very similar to the porbeagle shark.

Reproductive potential: Usually, the brood contains two to four young. The lengths of the reproductive and gestation cycles are unknown. According to Blagoderov (1994), juveniles under 60 cm TL occur in only three regions: the open waters of the Pacific from 156^0E to 180^0E; the southern Kuril region; and the southern part of the Sea of Okhotst. The juveniles continue to reside there until they reach 110-120 cm TL.

Impact of fisheries: Large numbers are caught in gillnets designed to capture salmon in the Japanese high-seas salmon fisheries and in the Alaskan coastal summer fisheries (Urquhart 1981). There is little marketing of the species in North America and many specimens are discarded (Urquhart 1981). There have been studies on developing a fishery in Alaska, but the fisheries do not seem to have developed (Paust and Smith 1986).

Status: Category 1. This species has been placed in this category because of the lack of fisheries data.

Porbeagle (*Lamna nasus*)

The porbeagle is lamnid shark common in deep cold temperate waters of the North Atlantic, South Atlantic and South Pacific Oceans. It is highly esteemed for its flesh. There have been fisheries for this species in the North Atlantic for many years.

Reproductive potential: Very little is known about its reproductive processes. Aasen (1963) estimated that maturity was reached at 150-200 cm TL for males and 200-250 cm TL for females. This author estimated that porbeagles reach 20 years of age and "very likely 10 years more". Shann (1911) reported an embryo 61 cm TL and estimated that porbeagles were probably born at about 76 cm TL. Bigelow and Schroeder (1948) recorded a free-swimming specimen at 76 cm TL. Gauld (1989) gave the mean number of embryos in a sample of 12 females as 3.7 embryos. The frequency of reproduction is not known. According to Aasen (1963), it probably reproduces annually, but there is no direct evidence to support this claim. The nurseries are probably in continental waters, but there is little published data.

Impact of fisheries: The porbeagle is presently fished in northern Europe and along the northeastern coast of North America. The porbeagle shark has been exploited by Scandinavian fishermen, since the early 1800s (Gauld 1989). Directed fisheries for porbeagles in the North Sea and off the Scottish coast have been carried out this century by Norwegian and Danish fishermen, and to the south and west of England by the French (Gauld 1989). Gauld (1989)[3] gives the Norwegian porbeagle catch from 1926 to 1953 (Fig. 11) and Norwegian catch for 1954-84 (Fig. 12). The modern Norwegian fishery started in the 1920s and it has been the most intensive porbeagle fishery in the North Atlantic Ocean. Catches rose rapidly from 279 t in 1926 to a high of 3 884 t in 1933. Thereafter, catches declined steadily, with a period of more reduced catches caused by World War II. The fishery resumed in 1945 and reached a peak of 2 824 t in 1947 (Fig. 11). The fishery continued to decline

---

3 There are discrepancies between the Norwegian porbeagle landings reported by Gauld (1989) and those reported by ICES (1995) for some of the earlier years.

and the scarcity of porbeagles in Europe then forced the Norwegians to explore other grounds (Rae 1962). By 1961, Norwegians were fishing for porbeagles off Newfoundland and New England. By 1965, catches had declined and the vessels shifted to other species or moved west to Africa to fish for shortfin mako or swordfish. The Norwegian catch has declined from 207 t in 1970 to 25 t in 1994 (ICES 1995) and the Danish fishery has also showed a decline from 1954 to 1984 (Fig. 13). Currently, Norway is allowed a quota of 200 t of porbeagles in EC waters (Gauld 1989).

Status: Category 4. Intensive fisheries have depleted the stocks of porbeagles in a few years wherever they have existed, demonstrated that the species cannot withstand heavy fishing pressure.

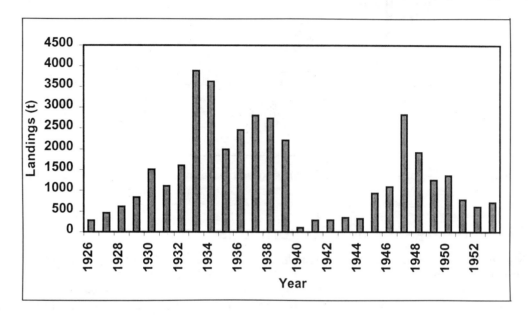

Figure 11. Total annual landings of porbeagles by Norway, 1926-53 (Gauld 1989).

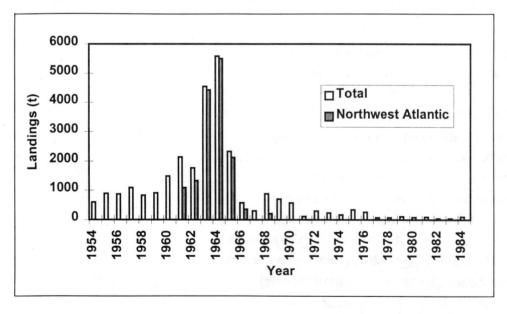

Figure 12. Reported landings of porbeagles during 1954-84, Norway (Gauld 1989).

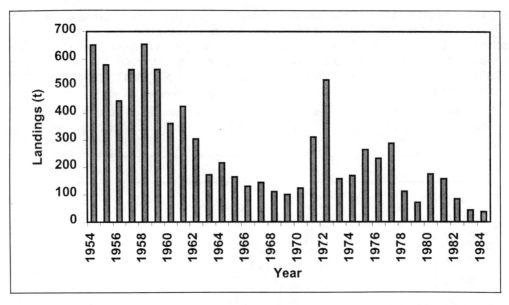

Figure 13. Reported landings of porbeagles by Denmark, 1954-84 (Gauld 1989).

4.2.23 Catsharks, Family Scyliorhinidae

The catsharks, family Scyliorhinidae, constitute the largest family of sharks. Catsharks are usually small, most are under 80 cm TL and some are full-grown at less than 40 cm TL. Many species are strikingly marked with lines or spots. They range in habitat from the intertidal zone to the deep continental slopes. Many dwell at depths of several hundred metres. Many species appear to have relatively very small ranges, but this may be an artefact or reflect the problems of catching small creatures at great depths. Because of their small size and deep-water habitat, catsharks are usually of no interest to fisheries, although many are caught as bycatch in bottom trawls or bottom-set longlines. We have no data to indicate that any of the following species are being exploited.

Not-exploited species:

Atlantic ghost shark (*Apristurus atlanticus*)

Brown catshark (*Apristurus brunneus*)

Hoary catshark (*Apristurus canutus*)

Longfin catshark (*Apristurus herklotsi*)

Smallbelly catshark (*Apristurus indicus*)

Broadnose catshark (*Apristurus investigatoris*)

Japanese catshark (*Apristurus japonicus*)

Longnose catshark (*Apristurus kampae*)

Iceland catshark (*Apristurus laurussoni*)

Longhead catshark (*Apristurus longicephalus*)

Flathead catshark (*Apristurus macrorhynchus*)

Madeira catshark (*Apristurus maderensis*)

Ghost catshark (*Apristurus manis*)

Smalleye catshark (*Apristurus microps*)

Largenose catshark (*Apristurus nasutus*)

Smallfin catshark (*Apristurus parvipinnis*)

Spatulasnout catshark (*Apristurus platyrhynchus*)

Deepwater catshark (*Apristurus profundorum*)

Broadgill catshark (*Apristurus riveri*)

Saldanha catshark (*Apristurus saldanha*)

Pale catshark (*Apristurus sibogae*)

South China catshark (*Apristurus sinensis*)

Spongehead catshark (*Apristurus spongiceps*)

Panama ghost catshark (*Apristurus stenseni*)

Borneo catshark (*Apristurus verweyi*)

Australian spotted catshark (*Asymbolus analis*)

Gulf catshark (*Asymbolus vincenti*)

Australian marbled catshark (*Atelomycterus macleayi*)

Coral catshark (*Atelomycterus marmoratus*)

Blackspotted catshark (*Aulohalaelurus labiosus*)

Reticulated swellshark (*Cephaloscyllium fasciatum*)

Draughtsboard shark (*Cephaloscyllium isabellum*)

Australian swellshark (*Cephaloscyllium laticeps*)

Whitefinned swellshark (*Cephaloscyllium nascione*)

Indian swellshark (*Cephaloscyllium silasi*)

Balloon shark (*Cephaloscyllium sufflans*)

Swellshark (*Cephaloscyllium ventriosum*)

Lollipop catshark (*Cephalurus cephalus*)

Roughtail catshark (*Galeus arae*)

Australian sawtail catshark (*Galeus boardmani*)

Gecko catshark (*Galeus eastmani*)

Blackmouth catshark (*Galeus melastomus*)

Mouse catshark (*Galeus murinus*)

Broadfin sawtail catshark (*Galeus nipponensis*)

Peppered catshark (*Galeus piperatus*)

African sawtail catshark (*Galeus polli*)

Blacktip sawtail catshark (*Galeus sauteri*)

Dwarf sawtail catshark (*Galeus schultzi*)

Arabian catshark (*Halaelurus alcocki*)

Speckled catshark (*Halaelurus boesemani*)

Blackspotted catshark (*Halaelurus buergeri*)

Dusky catshark (*Halaelurus canescens*)

New Zealand catshark (*Halaelurus dawsoni*)

Bristly catshark (*Halaelurus hispidus*)

Spotless catshark (*Halaelurus immaculatus*)

Lined catshark (*Halaelurus lineatus*)

Mud catshark (*Halaelurus lutarius*)

Tiger catshark (*Halaelurus natalensis*)

Quagga catshark (*Halaelurus quagga*)

Puffadder shyshark (*Haploblepharus edwardsii*)

Brown shyshark (*Haploblepharus fuscus*)

Dark shyshark (*Haploblepharus pictus*)

African spotted catshark (*Holohalaelurus punctatus*)

Izak catshark (*Holohalaelurus regani*)

Campeche catshark (*Parmaturus campechiensis*)

Blackgill catshark (*Parmaturus melanobranchius*)

Salamander catshark (*Parmaturus pilosus*)

Filetail catshark (*Parmaturus xaniurus*)

Onefin catshark (*Pentanchus profundicolus*)

Striped catshark (*Poroderma africanum*)

Barbeled catshark (*Poroderma marleyi*)

Leopard catshark (*Poroderma pantherinum*)

Narrowmouthed catshark (*Schroederichthys bivius*)

Redspotted catshark (*Schroederichthys chilensis*)

Narrowtail catshark (*Schroederichthys maculatus*)

Slender catshark (*Schroederichthys tenuis*)

Polkadot catshark (*Scyliorhinus besnardi*)

Boa catshark (*Scyliorhinus boa*)

Small-spotted catshark (*Scyliorhinus canicula*)

Yellowspotted catshark (*Scyliorhinus capensis*)

West African catshark (*Scyliorhinus cervigoni*)

Brownspotted catshark (*Scyliorhinus garmani*)

Freckled catshark (*Scyliorhinus haeckelii*)

Whitesaddled catshark (*Scyliorhinus hesperius*)

Blotched catshark (*Scyliorhinus meadi*)

Chain catshark (*Scyliorhinus retifer*)

Nursehound (*Scyliorhinus stellaris*)

Cloudy catshark (*Scyliorhinus torazame*)

Dwarf catshark (*Scyliorhinus torrei*)

4.2.24 Finback catsharks, Family Proscylliidae

This is a small family of small deep-water sharks. They are of no interest to fisheries.

Not-exploited species:

Harlequin catshark (*Ctenacis fehlmanni*)

Cuban ribbontail catshark (*Eridacnis barbouri*)

Pygmy ribbontail catshark (*Eridacnis radcliffei*)

African ribbontail catshark (*Eridacnis sinuans*)

Slender smooth-hound (*Gollum attenuatus*)

Graceful catshark (*Proscyllium habereri*)

4.2.25 False catsharks, Family Pseudotriakidae

False catshark (*Pseudotriakis microdon*)

The false catshark is a rare, large, deep-water species. It has worldwide distribution usually found at depths of 350-1500 m.

Status: Not-exploited species.

4.2.26   Barbeled houndsharks, Family Leptochariidae

Barbeled houndshark (*Leptocharias smithii*)

This is a small, common, inshore, tropical shark of the West African shelves, found near the bottom at depths of 10-75m (Compagno 1984). We have no data on its fisheries.

Status: Category 1.

4.2.27   Smooth-hounds or houndsharks, Family Triakidae

The smooth-hounds are small to medium size sharks that inhabit shallow to moderately deep waters. Some have local economic importance.

Not-exploited species:

Sailback houndshark (*Gogolia filewoodi*)
Longnose houndshark (*Iago garricki*)
Flapnose houndshark (*Scylliogaleus quecketti*)
Sharpfin houndshark (*Triakis acutipinna*)
Spotted houndshark (*Triakis maculata*)

Category 1:

Japanese topeshark (*Hemitriakis japanica*)
Whitefin topeshark (*Hemitriakis leucoperiptera*)
Blacktip tope (*Hypogaleus hyugaensis*)
Bigeye houndshark (*Iago omanensis*)
Starry smooth-hound (*Mustelus asterias*)
Grey smooth-hound (*Mustelus californicus*)
Dusky smooth-hound (*Mustelus canis*)
Sharptooth smooth-hound (*Mustelus dorsalis*)
Striped smooth-hound (*Mustelus fasciatus*)
Spotless smooth-hound (*Mustelus griseus*)
Brown smooth-hound (*Mustelus henlei*)
Smalleye smooth-hound (*Mustelus higmani*)
Spotted estuary smooth-hound (*Mustelus lenticulatus*)
Sicklefin smooth-hound (*Mustelus lunulatus*)
Starspotted smooth-hound (*Mustelus manazo*)
Speckled smooth-hound (*Mustelus mento*)
Arabian smooth-hound (*Mustelus mosis*)
Smooth-hound (*Mustelus mustelus*)
Narrowfin smooth-hound (*Mustelus norrisi*)
Whitespotted smooth-hound (*Mustelus palumbes*)
Blackspotted smooth-hound (*Mustelus punctulatus*)
Humpback smooth-hound (*Mustelus whitneyi*)
Sharptooth houndshark (*Triakis megalopterus*)
Banded houndshark (*Triakis scyllium*)

Whiskery shark (*Furgaleus macki*)

The whiskery shark occurs predominantly in Western Australian waters, south of Shark Bay, but also occurs in small numbers in South Australia, Victoria, and Tasmania. The whiskery sharks live on the bottom or near the bottom to the depth of about 220 m (Last and Stevens 1994).

Reproductive potential: The biology of the whiskery shark is poorly known. They are born at about 25 cm TL, mature at approximately 120 cm TL, and grow to a maximum of 160 cm TL. Females are believed to produce broods of 4-24 (average 19) young every second year. The females probably give birth in the spring or early summer (Last and Stevens 1994).

Impact of fisheries: The whiskery shark is locally important in the Western Australia fishery (Walker *et al.*1996b). Although previously caught in commercial quantities in South Western Australia (Fig. 14), there are concerns about declining CPUE in most sectors of the fishery (Stevens 1993).

Status: Category 4. According to the Fisheries Department of Western Australia stock assessment of 1995, the best estimates of the current biomass level indicate that the whiskery shark stock is currently over-exploited (i.e. is less than 40% of the unexploited stock size). Reductions in the total allowable effort in the area have achieved some reductions in catch, but the effects of these reductions are unknown at this time. Last and Stevens (1994) state that the fishery is now thought to be fully exploited, with signs of overfishing.

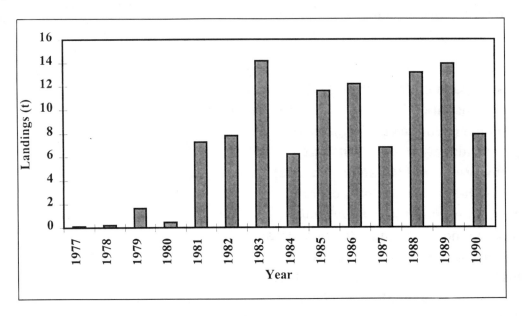

Figure 14. South Australia landings (whole weight) of whiskery sharks, 1977-90 (Stevens 1993).

Tope shark (*Galeorhinus galeus*)

The tope shark is a small coastal shark found in temperate waters 10-22°C throughout the world. It is a very slow growing species, having a late age at maturity and a natural longevity of some 60 years (Stevens 1993). This is one of the best known sharks, primarily due to the work of Australian scientists. The wealth of information on this species can only be briefly summarized here. The reader is advised to consult the excellent summaries by Walker (1995b) and Walker *et al.* (1996a) for more information.

Reproductive potential: Males mature at 120 cm TL and females at 145 cm TL (Olsen 1984). The young are born at about 30 cm TL (Olsen 1984). Broods range from 15 to 43 young, with a mean of 30 (Walker 1995b). The gestation period is six months and reproduction is biennial (Olsen 1984). For age at maturity, see the discussion by Walker *et al.* (1996a). Olsen (1984) gave the von Bertalanffy growth parameters for combined sexes as L_∞= 160.04 cm, K= 0.1639 year^{-1}, t_0= -1.2669 years. The nurseries are located in shallow coastal waters (Walker 1995b).

Impact of fisheries: An intensive fishery for this species existed for a few years off the western coast of North America in the late 1930s and 1940s. By 1950, the fishery had collapsed due to overexploitation (Westrheim 1950). Although, nearly five decades have passed since the fishery ceased, the stocks have not recovered (B. Lea, California Dept. Fish and Game, pers. comm.). The tope has been exploited intensively off Australia and New Zealand, since the 1940s where it is known as the school shark. In 1992, 1 718 t of tope were taken by the Australian eastern shark fishery and about another 50 t were taken by other target and bycatch fisheries (Stevens 1993). It is currently considered overfished in the Australian southeastern shark fishery (Fig. 15). The best estimate of maximum sustainable yield is about 825 t whole weight. The tope has been managed in Australia for many years. A new management regime is being implemented to improve the stocks. In New Zealand, catches peaked in 1984 with 4 941 t whole weight and have decreased to 2 483 t by 1992 (Stevens 1993). In France, tope catches peaked at about 1 100 t in 1982 and have decreased steadily to 225 t by 1992 (Muñoz-Chapuli *et al.* 1993). The stocks are considered very reduced in Brazil (Amorim and Arfelli 1993). It is suspected of being overexploited in Argentina (Chiaramonte pers. comm.).

Status: Category 4. We consider it Category 4, because it is a very slow growing species, it is the object of intensive fisheries in may parts of its range, and it is already considered overfished in some areas. The experience in the western United States with this species demonstrates that overfished stocks may not recover for many decades.

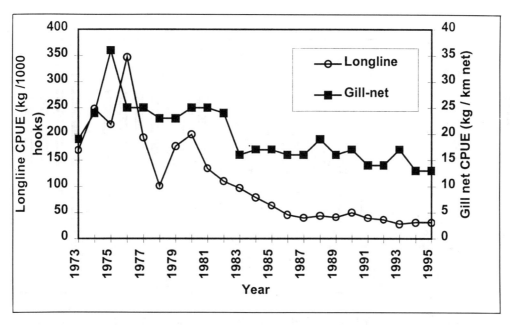

Figure 15. Tope shark CPUE by fishing method for South Australia, Victoria, and Tasmania, 1973-95 (Walker *et al.* 1996b).

Gummy shark (*Mustelus antarcticus*)

The gummy shark is a bottom dwelling species found in the intertidal zone to about 183 m (Compagno 1984, Last and Stevens 1994). It inhabits the waters of the western South Pacific, including areas of Western and South Australia, Queensland, Victoria, Tasmania and New South Wales.

Reproductive Biology: The gummy shark males reach about 145 cm TL, while females reach about 177 cm TL (Walker 1995a). Males mature around 93 cm TL and the females around 130 cm TL (Last and Stevens 1994). Moulton *et al.* (1992) stated that males mature at about 13+ years old and the females at 16+ years old, and gave the von Bertalanffy parameters for the males as L_∞= 141.7 cm, K= 0.170 year^{-1}, t_0= -2.08 years (from 516 observations), and for the females: L_∞= 201.9, K= 0.086, t_0= -0.301 (from 752 observations). The length of the breeding cycle is not certain. Walker (1995a) suggested that the breeding cycle is biennial in the Bass Strait population and annual in the southern and western Australian populations. The brood size ranges from 1 to 38 young, with the mean birth length of 33 cm TL (Walker 1995a). The juvenile sharks are known to collect in shallow waters, but there is no known well defined nursery ground areas (Walker 1995a).

Impact of fisheries: Gummy sharks, in combination with tope sharks, are very heavily fished in southeastern and Western Australian fisheries and the surrounding states. Walker (1995a) reported that those two species constituted 88 percent of the 1974-1994 total shark catch South Australia, Tasmania, and Victoria. During this same time period, only 12 percent of the gummy shark was caught with longlines, and the majority was fished by gillnets. In 1993, the gross value of production in the southern shark fishery was estimated at $13.9 million, approximately $8.3 million can be attributed to gummy sharks (Walker 1995a). In 1986, at the Third Meeting of the Southern Shark Assessment Workshop, it was recommended that the stocks of the gummy shark be managed and reduce fishing effort to the standards in 1982. The Southern Shark Fishery Advisory Group (SharkFAG) has reviewed the gummy shark population in Bass Strait and recognizes the current biomass to be 40-55% of the initial biomass. They also have indicated the fishery is sustainable at the current level of effort (Fig. 16).

Status: Category 3. The Southern Shark Fishery Assessment Group assessed the gummy shark stocks as generally sound (Walker 1995a). However, Walker *et al.* (1996b) showed that the CPUE of the gummy shark declined severely during 1973-87 (Fig. 17). According to Last and Stevens (1994), the species has been heavily exploited since the 1970s and is currently overfished. The gummy shark production from Victorian inlets exemplifies this situation (Fig. 18).

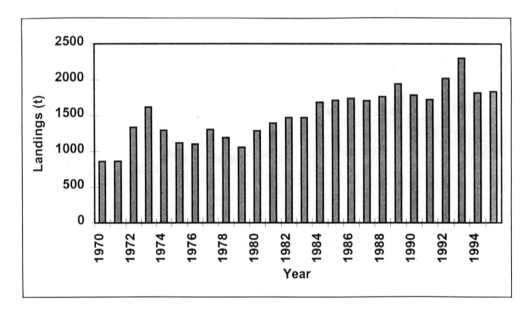

Figure 16. Gummy shark landings (carcass weight t) for South Australia, Victoria, and Tasmania, 1970-95 (Walker *et al.*1996b).

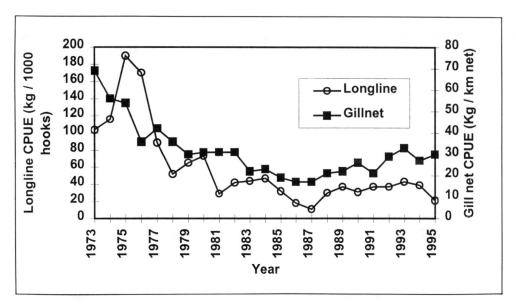

Figure 17. Gummy shark CPUE by fishing method for South Australia, Victoria, and Tasmania, 1973-95 (Walker *et al.*1996b).

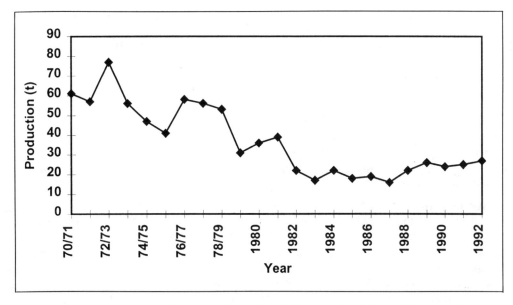

Figure 18. Production of the gummy shark (carcass wt) from Victorian inlets 1970-1992 (Stevens 1993).

Narrownose smooth-hound (*Mustelus schmitti*)

The narrownose smooth-hound is a common, small, bottom-dwelling shark of the continental shelf of Atlantic South America (Compagno 1984).

Reproductive potential: Menni (1986) gave the calculated length at maturity as 62 cm TL for females and 60 cm TL for males. Ficher (1996) gave the age at maturity for both males and females as six years, and stated that the oldest females reach 22 years and males reach 21 years. Broods range from 2 to 13, with 4 being the usual number (Menni 1986).

Impact of fisheries: The species is exploited in Brazil, Uruguay, and Argentina. In Argentina, the Instituto Nacinal de Investigacion y desarrollo Pesquero (INIDEP) estimated a mean annual biomass of 76 000 t, and a maximal sustainable yield of 19 000 t (manuscript, G. Chiaramonte, Museo Argentino de Ciencias Naturales, Buenos Aires).

Status: Category 2. Based on available FAO statistics for this fishery in Argentina (Fig. 19) and estimates of MSY, exploitation of the stock in this area appears sustainable. However, because the species is exploited over a wide area, full catch and effort statistics are needed from Brazil to Argentina, before final conclusions can be reached on the management of the fishery (Ficher 1996).

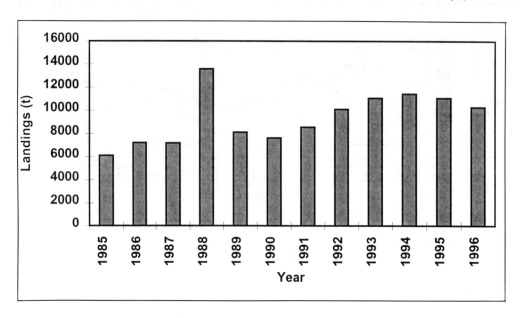

Figure 19. Narrownose smooth-hound landings from Argentina, FAO Area 41, 1985-1996 (FAO 1996, 1998).

Leopard shark (*Triakis semisfasciata*)

The leopard shark is a common species found in shallow inshore waters of the western coast of North America (Miller and Lea 1972, Castro 1983). It ranges from Oregon (USA) to Mexico. It is often found in large schools. It is very abundant off California, where it is the target of both commercial and recreational fisheries (Holts 1988).

Reproductive potential: According to Kusher *et al.* (1992), males mature between 100 and 105 cm TL and 0.63 to 0.66 of their asymptotic length, and at ages of 7-13 years; females mature between lengths of 105 and 135 cm TL, or between 0.72 and 0.93 of their asymptotic lengths, at ages of 10-15 years. Kusher *et al.* (1992) gave the following growth parameters: L_∞ = 153.6 cm, K= 0.082 year^{-1}, and t_0 = -2.31 years. According to Smith (1984) the maximum validated age was 16 years. A demographic analysis by Cailliet (1992) yielded a net reproductive rate (R_0) of 4.467, a generation time of 22.35 years, and an estimate of the instantaneous population growth coefficient (r) of 0.067 year^{-1} The young measure 18-20 cm TL at birth (Castro 1983). Broods range from 7 to 30 young, depending on the size of the female (Castro 1983). The gestation period is estimated to be one year (Ackerman 1971). Nursery areas are in shallow coastal waters such as San Francisco, Tomales, and Bodega bays (Castro 1983).

Impact of fisheries: Both recreational and commercial fisheries for this species have existed in California for many years. Reported commercial landings from California increased (Fig. 20) from 2.69 t in 1974 to 29.92 t in 1986 (Holts 1988). In 1992 California sports-fishing regulations limit anglers to three sharks per trip and set a minimum size of 91.4 cm TL (Cailliet 1992).

Status: Category 4. Kusher *et al.* (1992) suggested that the species is susceptible to overexploitation, because of its life history characteristics. We consider the species to be Category 4, because it is a slow-growing species of limited reproductive potential that is targeted by both commercial and recreational fisheries, and has its nurseries in shallow coastal waters adjacent to highly populated areas that are subject to intensive fishing.

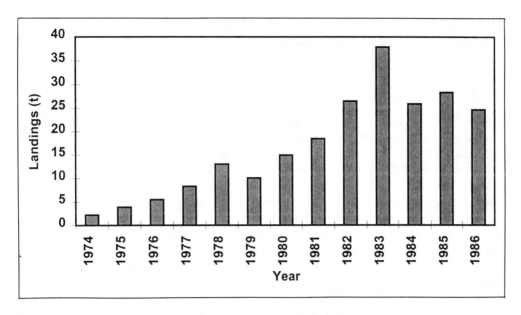

Figure 20. Commercial leopard shark landings, Unites States and Mexico (Holts 1988).

4.2.28 Weasel sharks, Family Hemigaleidae

This is a small family of tropical sharks of the Indo-West Pacific. We do not have sufficient information to evaluate them.

Category 1:

Hooktooth shark (*Chaenogaleus macrostoma*)

Sicklefin weasel shark (*Hemigaleus microstoma*)

Snaggletooth shark (*Hemipristis elongatus*)

Atlantic weasel shark (*Paragaleus pectoralis*)

Straight-tooth weasel shark (*Paragaleus tengi*)

4.2.29 Requiem sharks, Family Carcharhinidae

The requiem sharks, also known as carcharhinids, whaler sharks, or grey sharks comprise one of the largest families of sharks. They are small to large sharks found in warm to temperate waters. This is the most economically important family of sharks, as many species are used for food, fins, leather, etc. Some species are wide-ranging or cosmopolitan.

Category 1:

Broadfin shark (*Lamiopsis temmincki*)

Sliteye shark (*Loxodon macrorhinus*)

Whitenose shark (*Nasolamia velox*)

Sicklefin lemon shark (*Negaprion acutidens*)

Milk shark (*Rhizoprionodon acutus*)

Brazilian sharpnose shark (*Rhizoprionodon lalandii*)

Pacific sharpnose shark (*Rhizoprionodon longurio*)

Grey sharpnose shark (*Rhizoprionodon oligolinx*)

Caribbean sharpnose shark (*Rhizoprionodon porosus*)

Australian sharpnose shark (*Rhizoprionodon taylori*)
Spadenose shark (*Scoliodon laticaudus*)
Whitetip reef shark (*Triaenodon obesus*)

Blacknose shark (*Carcharhinus acronotus*)

The blacknose shark is a common coastal species that inhabits the western North Atlantic from North Carolina to southeastern Brazil (Bigelow and Schroeder 1948). It is very abundant in coastal waters from the Carolinas to Florida and the Gulf of Mexico during summer and fall (Castro 1983). Schwartz (1984) hypothesized that there are two separate populations in the western Atlantic, but this has not been confirmed.

Reproductive potential: Maturity is reached at about 100 cm TL. Broods consist of 3-6 young that measure 50 cm TL at birth (Castro 1983). Dodrill (1977) estimated the gestation period to be 10-11 months and suggested that the breeding cycle was biennial. Schwartz (1984) estimated that the largest adult male captured was 164 cm TL was 9.6 years old, while an adult female 154 cm TL was also 9.6 years old. Castro (1983) stated that the nursery areas were in the shallow waters of South Carolina (USA)

Impact of fisheries: Very large numbers of blacknose sharks are caught in shallow coastal waters of the southeastern United States. Although, the blacknose shark shows typical carcharhinid characteristics, such as biennial reproductive cycle, in the United States Fishery Management Plan for Sharks of the Atlantic Ocean (FMP), the blacknose shark is included in the "small coastal sharks". This category of "small coastal sharks" includes species, such as the Atlantic sharpnose shark and the bonnethead, which have much different yearly reproductive cycles.

Status: Category 3. We consider it a Category 3 species, because it has typical carcharhinid characteristics such as biennial reproductive cycle, and it is the target of unrestricted fisheries in the United States.

Silvertip shark (*Carcharhinus albimarginatus*)

The silvertip shark is widespread in the warm Pacific and Indian Oceans (Bass *et al.* 1973). In the Pacific, it is common near the eastern tropical islands, such as Galapagos and Revillagigedo, but is relatively rare in the nearby inshore localities off Central and South America (Beebe and Tee-Van 1941).

Reproductive potential: Males mature at about 180 cm TL, and a 199 cm TL female was reported as mature. Young are born at 70-80 cm TL. Broods range from 1 to 10 young and the average is 5.5 (Bass *et al.* 1973).

Impact of fisheries: This species has been reported as one of the more abundant sharks taken at different locations such as Mauritius, where it comprised 38% of 1 138 sharks taken (Bass *et al.* 1973) and in St. Brandon, where it comprised 44% of 57 sharks taken (Bass 1970).

Status: Category 1.

Bignose shark (*Carcharhinus altimus*)

The bignose shark is a bottom dwelling shark of the deeper parts of the continental shelves in tropical and subtropical waters throughout the world (Castro 1983).

Reproductive potential: The smallest mature specimens recorded by Springer (1960) were a 213 cm TL male and a 221 cm TL female. Springer (1950c) reported broods of 7 to 8 young, and Stevens and McLoughlin (1991) as 3 to 15 young. Birth size is probably around 70 cm TL based on the largest embryos (65-70 cm TL) reported by Fourmanoir (1961) and free swimming specimens with fresh umbilical scars seen by Bass *et al.* (1973). The lengths of the gestation period and of the breeding cycle have not been reported.

Impact of fisheries: Springer (1950c) stated that the bignose shark appeared to be the most common large shark on the edges of the continental shelves in the West Indian region, and that the species made up a substantial portion of the catch in the Florida shark fishery of the 1940s. Berkeley and Campos (1988) reported that bignose sharks constituted 2.8 % of the sharks caught in swordfish longlines along the east coast of Florida in 1981-83. Interestingly, Anderson and Ahmed (1993) reported that fishermen in the Maldives catch them on pelagic longlines, and that its presence was widespread in the fisheries. Stevens and McLoughlin (1991) also reported catching bignose sharks near the surface in northern Australia. Although, this is a common species caught in many longline fisheries we have no data on catches or landings. In some areas, bignose sharks are mistaken for sandbar sharks and this may create some confusion.

Status: Category 1.

Graceful shark (*Carcharhinus amblyrhynchoides*)

This is a little-known, probably common, tropical, coastal pelagic shark of the continental shelves of the Indo-West Pacific (Compagno 1984).

Reproductive potential: According to Stevens and McLoughlin (1991), males mature at about 108 cm TL and females at about 115 cm TL. The same authors estimated the birth size at 50-60 cm TL and the gestation period at 9 to 10 months. Stevens and McLoughlin (1991) also reported a brood size range from 1 to 9 young with an average of 3. In their study, all mature females were pregnant, indicating an annual reproductive cycle.

Impact of fisheries: According to Compagno (1984), it is "apparently caught by fisheries off Sri Lanka, India, and the Gulf of Thailand". Stevens and McLoughlin (1991) reported that in Western Australia, it was taken at 7% of gill-net stations and 4% of hook and line stations in the 0-50 m depth zone. We have no other data.

Status: Category 1.

Grey reef shark (*Carcharhinus amblyrhynchos*)

The grey reef shark is common around coral reefs and in oceanic waters adjacent to them in the Indo-West Pacific region (Compagno 1984).

Impact of fisheries: Anderson and Ahmed (1993) reported that the grey reef shark forms a major part of catches by bottom set gillnet, bottom set longline and handline in the Maldives. We have no other fishery data on it, although it is obviously caught in the other islands of the region.

Status: Category 1.

Pigeye shark (*Carcharhinus amboinesis*)

This is a large inshore species of the Indo-Pacific region. It is often mistaken for the more common bull shark. We have no fisheries data for this species.

Status: Category 1.

Borneo shark (*Carcharhinus borneensis*)

This is a rare, coastal, inshore, tropical shark, its biology and fisheries are virtually unknown.

Status: Category 1.

Copper shark (*Carcharhinus brachyurus*)

This is a coastal-pelagic species of widespread distribution in warm temperate waters throughout the world. In general, it is a temperate shark, absent or rare in tropical waters (Bass *et al.* 1973).

Reproductive potential: Males mature between 200 and 220 cm TL, and females mature below 247 cm TL. The young are born at about 60-70 cm TL. Six pregnant females averaged 16 embryos, with a range of 13 to 20 young per brood (Bass *et al.* 1973). Age at sexual maturity was calculated by Walter and Ebert (1991) at 13-19 years for males and 19-20 years for females. Gestation is believed to last a year (Cliff and Dudley 1992). The length of the reproductive cycle is not known, but it is probably biennial like most large carcharhinid sharks.

Impact of fisheries: We have very little data on fisheries. Off Natal, South Africa, Cliff and Dudley (1992) reported that copper sharks constituted 9.6% of all sharks caught in the gill nets that protect the bathing beaches. In South Australia, there is a rapidly growing fishery (Fig. 21) for the copper shark (Stevens 1993).

Status: Category 3. We consider it Category 3, because it appears to be a very slow growing carcharhinid, based on the unvalidated ages by Walter and Ebert (1991).

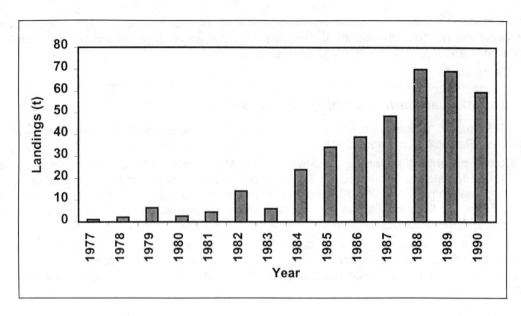

Figure 21. South Australian landings of copper (bronze whaler) sharks, 1977-90 (Stevens 1993).

Spinner shark (*Carcharhinus brevipinna*)

The spinner shark is a common, coastal-pelagic, warm-temperate and tropical shark of the continental and insular shelves (Compagno 1984). It is seen in schools, often leaping out of the water while spinning. It is a migratory species, but its movement patterns are poorly known. In eastern North America it ranges from North Carolina to Florida, and the Gulf of Mexico.

Reproductive potential: Males mature at 130 cm TL or 4-5 years, females mature at 150-155 cm TL or 7-8 years (Branstetter 1987a). According to this author, males reach maximum size at 10-15 years and females at 15-20 years. However, he added the caveat that "as sharks near their maximum size, growth is slower, therefore their maximum ages may be much greater". Branstetter (1987a) gave von Bertalanffy parameters for both sexes were: L_∞= 214 cm, K= 0.212 year^{-1}, t_0 = -1.94 years. The ages have not been validated. According to Garrick (1982), the species reaches 278 cm TL. The young are born at 60-75 cm TL in late May and early June. The broods usually consist of 6-12 young (Castro 1983). It has a biennial reproductive cycle (Castro 1993b). The nursery areas are in shallow coastal waters (Castro 1993b).

Impact of fisheries: Unknown

Status: Category 1. The spinner shark is similar in reproductive potential and habits to the blacktip shark (*Carcharhinus limbatus*), and its vulnerability to fisheries is also probably very similar to that of the blacktip.

Nervous shark (*Carcharhinus cautus*)

This is a little known reef shark of the South Pacific Ocean (Compagno 1984). It is relatively common in the estuarine and inshore waters of northern Australia (Lyle 1987).

Reproductive potential: Males mature at about 80 cm TL and females mature at about 85 cm TL (Lyle 1987). Broods range from 1 to 5 young, the mode being 5. The gestation period is believed to last 8-9 months and the young are probably born at about 40 cm TL. Evidence suggests that the reproductive cycle is annual (Lyle 1987).

Impact of fisheries: The species is of little commercial importance (Lyle 1987).

Status: Not-exploited species.

Whitecheek shark (*Carcharhinus dussumieri*)

This is a small, very common, but little-known inshore shark of the Indo-West Pacific (Compagno 1984). The species is available to artisanal fisheries wherever present, but we have no data on it.
Status: Category 1.

Silky shark (*Carcharhinus falcifomis*)

The silky shark inhabits warm tropical and subtropical waters throughout the world. Primarily, the silky is an offshore, epipelagic shark, but the juveniles venture inshore during the summer. The silky shark is one of the most abundant large sharks in the world.

Reproductive potential: Data on the silky shark are variable. There is a strong possibility that different populations across the oceans may vary in their reproductive potential. Broods range from six to fourteen young which measure 75-80 cm TL at birth (Castro 1983). According to Bonfil *et al.* (1993), the silky shark in the Campeche Bank, Mexico, has a twelve month gestation period, giving birth to 10-14 young with average of 76 cm TL during late spring and early summer, possibly every two years. Males mature at 225 cm TL (about 10 years) and females at 232-245 cm TL (>12 years old). The von Bertalanffy parameters estimated by Bonfil *et al.* (1993) are: L_∞= 311 cm TL, K= 0.101 year^{-1}, t_0= -2.718 years. Maximum ages determined from stained vertebral sections were 20+ years for males and 22+ years for females (Bonfil *et al.* 1993). Springer (1967) describes reefs on the outer continental shelf as nursery areas. Bonfil *et al.* (1993) mentions the Campeche Bank, as a prime nursery area in the Atlantic.

Impact of fisheries: The silky shark is one of the most abundant sharks caught in swordfish and tuna fisheries. Berkeley and Campos (1988) found it to constitute 27.2% of all sharks caught in swordfish vessels off the Florida east coast (USA) in 1981-83. Strasburg (1958) found the silky shark to comprise 52% of all sharks caught south of 10^0N latitude in the equatorial Pacific, in a sample of 4 157 sharks.

Status: Category 3. In spite of its abundance and frequency in the bycatch of tuna and swordfish fisheries, there is very little information on the silky shark catches. In the FAO data base, the only species specific landings for the silky come from Sri Lanka (Fig. 22). The silky shark is the most important shark species in Sri Lanka (D. Amarasooriya, National Aquatic Resources Agency, Sri Lanka, letter to FAO) and its landings in this country show a marked increase in recent years (FAO 1996, 1998). Given the lack of data, we can only quote Bonfil *et al.* (1993), "consider the life-history characteristics of slow growth, late maturation, and limited offspring, which point towards a very fragile resource. In all probability, local stocks of this species cannot support sustained heavy fishing pressure".

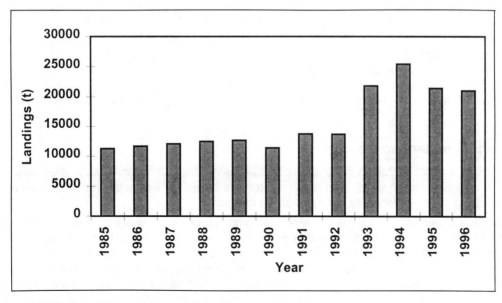

Figure 22. Silky shark landings from Sri Lanka, Area 51 (FAO 1996, 1998).

Creek whaler (*Carcharhinus fitzroyensis*)

This is a little-known tropical shark of the northern Australian littoral (Compagno 1984), which is common in estuarine and inshore waters (Lyle 1987). We have no data on fisheries.

Status: Category 1.

Galapagos shark (*Carcharhinus galapagensis*)

The Galapagos shark is circumtropical around oceanic islands (Castro 1983). It is very similar to the dusky shark and it is often confused with it. The Galapagos shark is found in the open ocean and around oceanic islands, while the dusky prefers continental shores (Castro 1983).

Reproductive potential: Males reach maturity between 205 and 239 cm TL and females between 215 and 245 cm TL (Wetherbee *et al.* 1996). Young are born at slightly over 80 cm TL and broods range from 4 to 16 young, the average being 8.7. The gestation cycle is estimated to last about a year (Wetherbee *et al.* 1996), but the length of the reproductive cycle is not known.

Impact of fisheries: We have no data on fisheries for the species. Because of its abundance around the islands where it lives, it is probably caught by longline fisheries.

Status: Category 1.

Pondicherry shark (*Carcharhinus hemiodon*)

This is a little-known shark of the Indo-West Pacific. We have no biological or fisheries data.
Status: Category 1.

Finetooth shark (*Carcharhinus isodon*)

This is common inshore species of the western Atlantic. It ranges from North Carolina to Brazil. It is abundant along the southeastern United States and the Gulf of Mexico (Castro 1983).

Reproductive potential: Males mature at about 130 cm TL and females mature at about 135 cm TL. The young measure 48-58 cm TL at birth. Broods range from 2 to 6 young, the average being 4 . The gestation period lasts about a year and the reproductive cycle is biennial. The nurseries are in shallow coastal waters (Castro 1993a).

Impact of fisheries: Large numbers of finetooth sharks are caught in gillnet fisheries off South Carolina, but most are not recorded by species (Castro pers. obs.). In the United States, the finetooth shark is included in the "small coastal sharks" category of the Fishery Management Plan for Sharks of the Atlantic Ocean. There is no quota limit for this category of "small coastal sharks", that includes species such as the Atlantic sharpnose shark and the bonnethead which have shorter gestation periods and much different yearly reproductive cycles. With its typical carcharhinid characteristics, such as biennial reproductive cycle, the finetooth shark is obviously misclassified.

Status: Category 3. The finetooth is caught in large numbers along the southeastern United States, but catches have gone unrecorded until very recent times. Until very recently some of those fisheries operated in the shallow nursery areas. Because of its classification as a "small coastal shark", there are no restrictions on catching this species in the United States. We consider it Category 3, because carcharhinid sharks with biennial reproductive cycles can not withstand unrestricted, intensive fisheries.

Bull shark (*Carcharhinus leucas*)

The bull shark is a large, shallow water shark that is cosmopolitan in warm seas and estuaries (Castro 1983). It often enters fresh water, and may penetrate hundreds of kilometres upstream. Although it is a very common species, very little is known about its habits.

Reproductive potential: Males mature at 210-220 cm TL or 14-15 years of age; females mature at >225 cm TL or 18+ years of age (Branstetter and Stiles 1987). Growth parameters have been estimated by Branstetter and Stiles (1987) as L_∞= 285 cm TL, K= 0.076 year^{-1}, t_0 = -3.0 years. Thorson and Lacy (1982), using tag-recapture methods and growth ring data, estimated that females reached "their larger size" at approximately 16 years and that males of maximum size were 12 years old. The young measure about 75 cm TL at birth (Clark and von Schmidt 1965). Jensen (1976) stated that broods ranged from 1 to 10 young and that the average size was 5.5. The gestation period is estimated at 10-11 months (Clark and von Schmidt 1965). The length of the reproductive cycle has not been published, but it is probably biennial. In the United States, the nursery areas are in low-salinity estuaries of the Gulf Coast (Castro 1983) and the coastal lagoons of the east coast of Florida (Snelson *et al.* 1984).

Impact of fisheries: The bull shark is a common coastal species that is fished in both artisanal and modern fisheries. Clark and von Schmidt (1965) found it to be the most common shark caught in their survey of the sharks of the central gulf coast of Florida, accounting for 18% of the shark catch. Dodrill (1977) reported it to be the seventh most commonly shark taken at Melbourne Beach, Florida, composing 8.6% of all longline landings. Kleijn (1974) found it to be one of the most common sharks taken by longline along the northeastern coast of South America. We have little published information on bull shark catches or fisheries. Thorson (1976) recorded a marked decline of the Lake Nicaragua-Rio, San Juan population from 1963 to 1974 resulting from a small-scale, but sustained commercial fishing operation. This fishery intensified in 1968 and by 1972 bull sharks in the area had become so scarce that Thorson (1976) predicted that any other developments would eliminate the bull shark from Lake Nicaragua. Russell (1993) indicated that the bull shark constituted 3% of the shark catch in the directed shark fishery in the US Gulf of Mexico. Castillo (1992) referred to the species in Mexico as "intensely exploited in both coasts".

Status: Category 3. We consider the bull shark Category 3, because it is a slow-growing species with a limited reproductive potential which is being pursued in numerous fisheries due to its abundance, near shore habitat and nurseries, and profitability due to its large size.

Blacktip shark (*Carcharhinus limbatus*)

The blacktip shark is circumtropical in shallow coastal waters and surface offshore waters of the continental shelves. Garrick (1982) on examining a large number of museum specimens of the blacktip shark, believed it to be a single worldwide species. Dudley and Cliff (1993) working on blacktips off South Africa and Castro (1996) working on blacktips off the southeastern United States, showed that there were significant differences among the various populations. The blacktip shark or "blacktip" is a fast moving shark that is often seen at the surface, frequently leaping and spinning out of the water. It often forms large schools at migration time. This is a much-sought species in the United States, because of the quality of its flesh. Its importance in that region is exceeded only by the sandbar shark. In the markets of the United States, "blacktip" has become synonymous with good quality shark, but a lot of other species are also sold under that name.

Reproductive potential: Off the southeastern United States males mature at between 142 and 145 cm TL and females mature at about 156 cm TL (Castro 1996). According to Branstetter and McEachran (1986), in the western North Atlantic, males mature at 139-145 cm TL at 4-5 years, and females at 153 cm TL at 6-7 years. These ages have not been validated and are based on a small sample. Branstetter and McEachran (1986) estimated the maximum age at 10 years, and gave the von Bertalanffy parameters for combined sexes as: L_∞= 171 cm, K= 0.284 year^{-1}, t_0= -1.5 years. Wintner and Cliff (1996), working on blacktips off the east coast of South Africa, gave the following von Bertalanffy parameters for combined sexes: L_∞= 193.6 cm PCL, K= 0.21, and t_0= -1.2. According to those authors, age at maturity was 7 years (156 cm PCL) for females and 6 years for males (150 cm PCL), and maximum ages were 11 years for females and 10 years for males. The young are born at 55-60 cm TL in late May and early June in shallow coastal nurseries from Georgia to the Carolinas (Castro 1996). Broods range from 1-8 young (Bigelow and Schroeder 1948) with the mean of 4 . The gestation cycle lasts about a year and the reproductive cycle is biennial (Castro 1996). Off South Africa, the blacktip reaches a much larger size. Dudley and Cliff (1993) gave the size at maturity for males as 199-204 cm TL and 205-211 cm TL for females.

Impact of fisheries: The blacktip is caught in many diverse fisheries throughout the world. Off the southeastern United States, it is usually caught in commercial longlines set in shallow coastal waters, but it is also pursued as a gamefish. There are localized gillnet fisheries in Florida that target blacktips during their migrations, when the schools are close to shore in clear waters. Aircraft are often used to direct net boats to the migrating schools, often resulting in the trapping of very large schools. In Georgia and the Carolinas, the blacktip is often caught in gillnets set in very shallow water. Cramer (1996a) reported a decrease in CPUE index from 0.4826 in 1992 to 0.2389 in 1995 in blacktip bycatch in the swordfish fishery off the western Atlantic coast of USA. Cramer (1996b) estimated the weight of sharks discarded dead by the same pelagic longline vessels, showing a decline from 1.34 t in 1992 to 0.29 t in 1995. Scott (1996) stated that there was a decrease in catch rates for blacktips in the southeastern United States marine recreational fishery since 1986, showing a CPUE index decrease from 18.23 in 1986 to 8.40 in 1995.

Status: Category 3. The species is considered Category 3, because it is pursued commercially throughout its range, it has a low reproductive potential, and it is often found in shallow coastal waters, where it is Category 4 to fisheries. Its habit of migrating in large schools along shorelines makes it extremely vulnerable to organized gillnet fisheries.

Oceanic whitetip shark (*Carcharhinus longimanus*)

The oceanic whitetip is one of the most common large sharks in warm oceanic waters (Castro 1983). It is circumtropical and it is nearly ubiquitous in water deeper than 180 m and temperatures above 21^0C.

Reproductive potential: Both males and females appear to mature at about 190 cm TL (Bass *et al.* 1973). Seki et al (1998) gave the von Bertalanffy growth parameters as: L_∞ = 244.58 cm, K= 0.103 $year^{-1}$, and t_0= 2.698 years. These authors gave the size at maturity for both males and females in the Pacific Ocean as 175-189 cm TL, corresponding to an age of 4-5 years of age. The young are born at about 65-75 cm TL (Castro 1983). In the Atlantic Ocean , the number of young per brood ranges from 2 to 10 with a mean of 6 (Backus *et al.* 1956, Guitart Manday 1975). Seki *et al.* (1998) examined 97 broods from the Pacific Ocean that ranged from 1 to 14 young, with a mode of 5 and an average of 6.2. The length of the gestation period has not been reported; it is probably 10-12 months like most large carcharhinids. The reproductive cycle is believed to be biennial (Backus *et al.* 1956). The location of the nurseries has not been reported. Preliminary work by the authors indicates that very young oceanic whitetip sharks are found well offshore along the southeastern United States in early summer, suggesting offshore nurseries over the continental shelves.

Impact of fisheries: Large numbers of oceanic whitetip sharks are caught as bycatch each year in pelagic tuna and swordfish fisheries. Strasburg (1958) reported that the oceanic whitetip shark constituted 28% of the total shark catch in exploratory tuna longline fishing south of 10^0 N latitude in the central Pacific Ocean. According to Berkeley and Campos (1988), oceanic whitetip sharks constituted 2.1% of the shark bycatch in the swordfish fishery along the east coast of Florida in 1981-83. Taniuchi (1990) reported that the oceanic whitetip shark constituted 3.4% of all sharks caught by some institutional tuna longline vessels operating from 1967 to 1968 in the Indian Ocean, 22.5% in the western Pacific Ocean, and 21.3% in the eastern Pacific Ocean. In the Maldives, Anderson and Ahmed (1993) reported that oceanic whitetip sharks were taken commercially by pelagic shark longliners and incidentally by tuna fishermen and that in a previous exploratory fishing survey oceanic whitetip sharks constituted 23% of all sharks caught. Guitart Manday (1975) demonstrated a marked decline in the oceanic whitetip shark landings in Cuba from 1971 to 1973.

Status: Category 3. Branstetter (1990) estimated the von Bertalanffy growth parameter K as 0.04-0.09 $year^{-1}$, and considered it a species with slow growth (a species with a growth parameter K<0.1). Seki *et al.* (1998) estimated K to be 0.103 $year^{-1}$, and using the same criterion, called it as a fast growth species. However, we consider the oceanic whitetip shark to be Category 3, because of its slow growth, limited reproductive potential, and because it is taken as bycatch in large numbers in various unrestricted pelagic fisheries and in directed fisheries.

Hardnose shark (*Carcharhinus macloti*)

This is a small, common but little-known inshore shark of the continental and insular shelves of the Indo-west Pacific (Compagno 1984). It is common in northern Australia.

Reproductive potential: Setna and Sarangdhar (1949) reported the size at maturity for males as 69 cm TL. Females were rare in their sample but the smallest gravid female was 76 cm TL. In northern Australia males mature at about 74 cm TL and the smallest gravid female was 78 cm TL (Stevens and McLoughlin 1991). The gestation period appears to last about 12 months, but the length of the reproductive cycle is not certain. The young are born at about 44 cm TL and broods consist of 1-2 young with a mean of 2 (Stevens and McLoughlin 1991).

Impact of fisheries: According to Lyle (1987), the hardnose shark constituted 14.6% of all fish caught by gillnet and 4.2% of those caught by longline in northern Australia, and represented an important component of the catches at all depths, being the third most abundant shark in his sample. Lyle (1987) stated that this species is commercially undesirable, because it is too small and has not been accepted by fish buyers in Australia.

Status: Category 1.

Blacktip reef shark (*Carcharhinus melanopterus*)

This is a small, common, tropical shark of Indo-Pacific waters (Compagno 1984). It is an inshore species, which comes into very shallow water on reef and sand flats, often with its dorsal fin exposed. It is often found around unpopulated or sparsely populated islands (Randall 1986).

Reproductive potential: Males mature at 91-100 cm TL and females mature at 96-112 cm TL. Young are born at varying lengths from 33-52 cm TL and broods range from 2 to 5 young (Randall 1986).

Impact of fisheries: According to Compagno (1984) this species is "apparently regularly caught where [it] occurs, including off India and Thailand", but we have no data on fisheries.

Status: Category 1.

Dusky shark (*Carcharhinus obscurus*)

The dusky shark is common in warm and temperate continental waters throughout the world. It is a migratory species moving north-south with the seasons. This is one of the larger species found from inshore waters to the outer reaches of continental shelves. It is important as a commercial species as well as a gamefish.

Reproductive potential: Males mature at about 279 cm TL and females mature at about 284 cm TL. These lengths correspond to 19 years for males and 21 years for females (Natanson *et al.* 1995). Broods consist of 6-14 young that measure 85-100 cm TL at birth (Castro 1983). The gestation period is believed to be about 16 months (Clark and von Schmidt 1965), but this needs confirmation. Natanson *et al.* (1995) gave the following parameters for males L_∞= 373 cm FL (449 cm TL), K= 0.038 year^{-1}, t_0= -6.28 years; and females at L_∞= 349 cm FL (421 cm TL), K= 0.039, t_0=-7.04. The growth rate is believed to be about 10 cm yr^{-1}. for the young and 5 cm yr^{-1}. for the adults. The nursery areas are in coastal waters. Castro (1993b) reported that dusky sharks gave birth in Bulls Bay, South Carolina, in April and May.

Impact of fisheries: The shark plays an important role in the coastal shark fisheries for flesh and fins, and is commonly taken as bycatch in the swordfish/tuna fisheries. Considering that the dusky shark is a cosmopolitan species, there is little published or recorded information known to the authors on the catch rates. Musick *et al.* (1993) reported CPUE decrease in the Chesapeake Bight region of the US mid-Atlantic coast from 1.73 sharks/100 hooks in the 1974-79 period to 0.0011 sharks/100 hooks in 1991. Russell (1993) reported a decrease in CPUE in tuna longline sets observed in the Gulf of Mexico, from 0.09 sharks/100 hooks in 1989, to 0.03 in 1990, to 0.0037 in 1991. Brown (1996) gave standardized CPUE for dusky sharks in the Virginia-Massachusetts area (USA) for the rod and reel fishery from 1986 to 1995 (Fig. 23). Cramer (1996a) found a similar decline in her analysis of logbooks from the US pelagic swordfish longline and coastal shark longlines from 1992 to 1995 (Fig. 24). Hueter (1991) noticed a marked decrease in the number of dusky sharks caught by a commercial fisherman (Crooke) off Pensacola (Florida, USA), from 1975 to 1989. After 1987 only one shark was caught. Since 1976, there has been an increase in the landings of dusky sharks in the southwestern fishery in Australia (Fig. 25). Stevens (1993) reports that the landings almost entirely consist of new-borns (0+ year class) from inshore nursery areas.

Status: Category 4. The dusky shark is one of the most slow growing requiem sharks and it is often caught on both coastal and pelagic longlines. The severe declines in North America and fishing of nursery areas in southwestern Australia indicate its high vulnerability to overfishing.

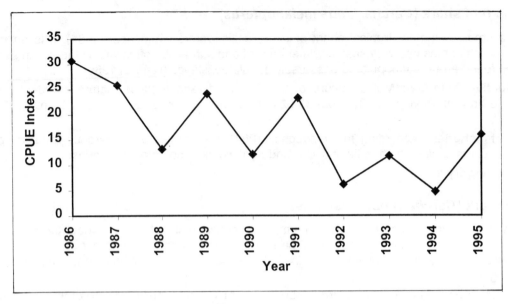

Figure 23. CPUE series for the dusky shark in the Unites States, Atlantic Ocean, 1986-95 (Brown 1996).

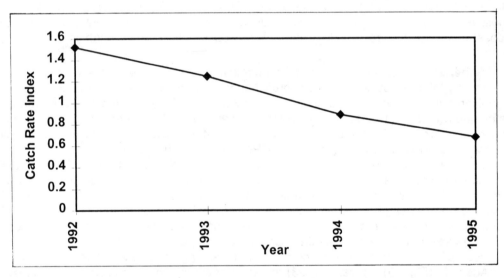

Figure 24. Catch rate index of the dusky shark in the western Atlantic, Gulf of Mexico, and Caribbean (Cramer 1996a).

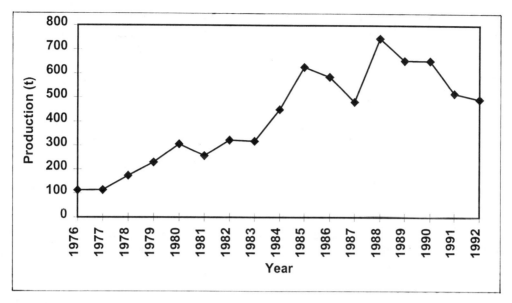

Figure 25. Dusky shark production off Western Australia (t whole weight) (Stevens 1993).

Caribbean reef shark (*Carcharhinus perezi*)

The Caribbean reef shark inhabits the southeastern coast of Florida, the Caribbean Sea, and the western Atlantic south to Brazil. This is a bottom-dwelling species that inhabits shallow coastal waters, usually around coral reefs (Castro 1983). It is a poorly known species.

Reproductive potential: Males mature about 170 cm TL and females at about 200 cm TL. Young are born at about 70 cm TL and broods consist of 4 to 6 young. The reproductive cycle is biennial (Castro unpublished data).

Impact of fisheries: Although this species is caught throughout the Caribbean, we have no data on fisheries.

Status: Category 1.

Sandbar shark (*Carcharhinus plumbeus*)

The sandbar shark is cosmopolitan in tropical and warm temperate waters. It is a common species found in many coastal habitats. It is a bottom-dwelling species most common in 20-55 m, but occasionally found at depths of about 200 m.

Reproductive potential: The sandbar is a very slow growing species. Both sexes reach maturity at about 180 cm TL (Castro 1983) or >136 cm PCL (Sminkey and Musick 1995). Estimates of age at maturity range from 15-16 years (Sminkey and Musick 1995) to 29-30 years (Casey and Natanson 1992). The von Bertalanffy growth parameters for combined sexes are L_∞= 186 cm, K= 0.046 year^{-1}, t_0= -6.45 years (Casey and Natanson 1992). Young are born at about 60 cm TL (smaller in the northern parts of the North American range), from March to July. Broods consist of 1-14 young with 9 being the average (Springer 1960). The gestation period lasts about a year and reproduction is biennial (Musick *et al.* 1993). Hoff (1990) used an age at maturity of 15 years, a life span of 35 years, and two-year reproductive cycle, to calculate that each female may reproduce only ten times. New maturity estimates and the increased mortality in the fishery may reduce that reproductive potential much further. In the United States, the sandbar shark has its nurseries in shallow coastal waters from Cape Canaveral, (Florida, USA) to Long Island, New York.

Impact of fisheries: It is the most important commercial species in the shark fishery of the southeastern United States. It is the preferred species in the area because it is the most abundant large shark, and because of the quality of its flesh and its large fins, both considered of the highest quality. Commercial longline fishermen pursue sandbar stocks in their north-south migrations along the coast, and their catches can be as much as 80-90% sandbar sharks in some areas. Large numbers of juvenile sandbar sharks were caught in gillnets set in shallow waters along the southeastern coast of the United States. Most of those gillnet fisheries have been outlawed by state governments. Musick *et al.* (1993) documented a severe decline in CPUE of the sandbar shark in the Chesapeake Bay area. A recent report by Ulrich (1996) showed a dramatic decline of sandbar sharks off South Carolina, catches decreasing from 4.73 sharks /100 hooks in 1983-84, to 0.41 sharks/100 hooks in 1993-94, to 0.39 sharks/100 hooks in 1994-95.

Status: Category 4. We consider the sandbar shark as Category 4, because if its slow maturation and historical declines in the US fishery.

Smalltail shark (*Carcharhinus porosus*)

This is a small, tropical and subtropical shark that inhabits shallow coastal waters and estuaries in the western Atlantic, from the Gulf of Mexico to southern Brazil, and the eastern Pacific from the Gulf of California to Peru (Castro 1983). Springer (1950a) referred to it as the commonest shark in the Gulf of Paria. The senior author observed this species to be the most abundant shark in Trinidad, where it was caught in very large numbers in gillnets set over muddy bottoms.

Reproductive potential: There are almost no published data on its reproductive processes. Females observed by the senior author in Trinidad were in different stages of gestation, suggesting a wide breeding season. Embryos up to 35 cm TL were observed. The reproductive cycle appears to be biennial.

Impact of fisheries: The species is marketed in many areas of Central America, Springer (1950a) stated that large numbers were sold in the Trinidad market. However, there is almost no published data on catches or landings.

Status: Category 1.

Blackspot shark (*Carcharhinus sealei*)

This is a common coastal shark of the continental and insular shelves of the Indo-West Pacific. It is usually found in shallow water, from the intertidal zone to about 40 m depth (Compagno 1984).

Reproductive potential: Maturity is reached at about 70 cm TL. Broods consist of 1-2 young. Parturition occurs throughout the year and females seem to have a continuous breeding cycle (Okera *et al.* 1981).

Impact of fisheries: We have no data on fisheries.

Status: Category 1.

Night shark (*Carcharhinus signatus*)

This carcharhinid shark inhabits the waters of the western North Atlantic from Delaware to Brazil and the western coast of Africa. It is a tropical species that seldom strays northward. It is usually found at depths greater than 275-366 m during the day and about 183 m at night (Castro 1983). It used to be a common bycatch of the American swordfish fishery.

Reproductive potential: There is little information on its reproductive processes. Broods usually consist of 12-18 young that measure 68-72 cm TL at birth (Castro 1983). There are no data on ageing or growth of the species.

Impact of fisheries: The night shark was abundant along the southeastern coast of the United States and the northwestern coast of Cuba before the development of the swordfish fishery of the 1970s. Martinez (1947) stated that the Cuban shark fishery relied heavily on the night shark, which constituted 60-75% of the total shark catch, and that the average annual catch for 1937-1941 was 12 000 sharks (Fig. 26). Most of the shark fishing was done along the northwestern coast of Cuba from some 70 rowboats, which landed as many as 150 night sharks a day. Guitart Manday (1975) documented a precipitous decline in night shark catches off the Cuban northwestern coast during the years 1971-1973. The mean weight of night sharks per unit of effort decreased from 53.34 kg in 1971, to 27.29 kg in 1972, and to 21.11 kg in 1973. Berkeley and Campos (1988) stated that this species represented 26.1% of all sharks caught in swordfish fisheries studied by them along the east coast of Florida from 1981 to 1983. Anecdotal evidence from commercial swordfish fishermen also indicates that, in the late 1970s, it was not unusual to have 50-80 dead night sharks, usually large gravid females, in every set from Florida to the Carolinas. During the 1970s, sports fishermen in South Florida often resorted to catching night sharks when other more desirable species (marlins) were not biting. The photographic record of sport fishing trophies shows that large night sharks were caught daily and landed at the Miami docks in the 1970s. Today the species is rare along the southeastern coast of the United States. In a NOAA survey of sharks in 1991 (Delaware II cruise DE II 91-06) of

439 sharks caught only 2 were night sharks (0.005%). The NOAA observer programme recorded only 1 night shark out of 362 sharks (0.28%) in 1993, and 10 night shark out of 295 shark sampled (3.39%) caught in commercial swordfish and tuna longline catches in 1994 (Dennis Lee, SEFSC, pers. comm.).

Status: Category 4. Unfortunately, there have been no studies on the species, and the available data is fragmentary and of disparate origins. Nevertheless, the decline of the night shark is one of the most dramatic examples of how a species caught as bycatch can decline and disappear before anything is known about its biology.

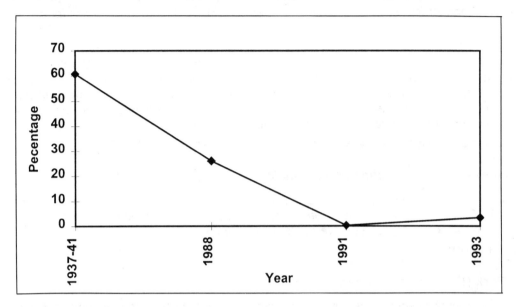

Figure 26. Night sharks as percentage of all sharks caught in the S.E. United States and Cuba. Years not to scale (From various sources; see text).

Spot-tail shark (*Carcharhinus sorrah*)

This is a common, coastal, shallow-water shark of the tropical Indo-West Pacific (Compagno 1984). It is often found in shallow water or around coral reefs (Bass *et al.* 1973).

Reproductive potential: In Australia, males mature at 90 cm TL and females mature at about 95 cm TL (Davenport and Stevens 1988). The young are born at 50-60 cm TL (Bass *et al.* 1973), and broods range from 1 to 8 young with a mean of 3.1 (Stevens and Wiley 1986). The gestation period is 10 months and the reproductive cycle is believed to be annual (Stevens and Wiley 1986). The von Bertalanffy growth parameters are for females L_∞= 123.9 cm, K= 0.34 year^{-1}, t_0= -1.9 years, and for males, L_∞= 98.4, K= 1.17, t_0= -0.6 . The maximum age recorded for the spot-tail is 7 years for females and 5 years for males. Sexual maturity is reached at the ages of 2-3 years for females (Davenport and Stevens 1988).

Impact of fisheries: The spot-tail shark was an important component of the Taiwanese fishery that operated in northern Australia (CSIRO 1990). The spot-tail shark landings in the Australian Fisheries Zone by Taiwanese vessels averaged 1 676 t annually from 1977 to 1984. The CPUE for sharks in that fishery (*Carcharhinus tilstoni* and *Carcharhinus sorrah* combined) decreased to nearly a quarter of its 1979 value by 1984, indicating that the removal rates were too high (CSIRO 1990). The species is also one of the preferred sharks in the markets of southern India (Frej and Gustafsson 1990). The species is also found in the commercial catch in the Maldives (Anderson and Ahmed 1993).

Status: Category 3. Although this is a fast growing species, based on the unvalidated age estimates by Davenport and Stevens (1988), that appears to reproduce annually, we consider it Category 3 because its reproductive potential is too low to replace the numbers of individuals taken by intensive, unrestricted fisheries.

Australian blacktip (*Carcharhinus tilstoni*)[4]

Carcharhinus tilstoni is found in the continental shelf waters of tropical Australia. The southern limits of its distribution are uncertain, because of previous confusion with the blacktip shark *(Carcharhinus limbatus)*.

Reproductive potential: Males reach maturity at about 105 cm TL, females reach maturity at about 105-110 cm TL. The young are born at about 60 cm TL, broods range from 1 to 8 young with an average of 4. Gestation lasts about 10 months and the reproductive cycle is annual (Stevens and Wiley 1986). The von Bertalanffy growth parameters for the males are L_∞ = 194.2 cm, K= 0.14 year^{-1}, t_0= -2.8 years, and for females L_∞= 165.4, K= .19, t_0= -2.6. The oldest recorded ages for the Australian blacktip are 12 years for females and 8 years for males. Maturity is reached by ages 3-4 (Davenport and Stevens 1988).

Impact of fisheries: In Australia, the species is managed as a unit with *Carcharhinus sorrah*. According to CSIRO (1990) the Australian gill net fishery appears to be currently under-exploiting the shark stocks in inshore northern waters. Between 1984-89 the combined catch of *C. tilstoni* and *C. sorrah* did not exceed 500 t annually. Population estimates from tagging suggest that the maximum sustainable catch for both species combined should be about 1 500 t live weight.

Status: Category 2. Our evaluation is based on the CSIRO assessment (1990).

Blacktail reef shark (*Carcharhinus wheeleri*)

This is a poorly known, medium sized shark of the Red Sea and the western Indian Ocean (Garrick 1982).   It is a common coastal species, probably relatively important to fisheries in some areas where it occurs (Compagno 1984), but we have no data on fisheries.

Status: Category 1.

Tiger shark (*Galeocerdo cuvier*)

The tiger shark inhabits warm waters in both deep oceanic and shallow coastal regions (Castro 1983). It is one of the larger species of sharks, reaching over 550 cm TL and over 900 kg. Its characteristic tiger-like markings and unique teeth make it one of the easiest sharks to identify. It is one of the most dangerous sharks and is believed to be responsible for many casualties (Castro 1983). Although the species is abundant and cosmopolitan in warm waters, its biology is poorly understood.

Reproductive potential: Tiger sharks mature at about 290 cm TL (Castro 1983, Simpfendorfer 1992). The young measure 68-85 cm TL at birth. Broods are large, usually consisting of 35-55 young (Castro 1983). According to Branstetter *et al.* (1987), in the Gulf of Mexico, males mature in 7 years and females in 8 years, and in the Atlantic they both mature in approximately 10 years. The largest male and female examined (381 cm TL) were 15 and 16 years of age respectively. The ages have not been validated. Branstetter *et al.* (1987) gave the growth parameters for an Atlantic sample as L_∞ = 440 cm TL, K= 0.107 year^{-1}, t_0= -2.35 years, and for a Gulf of Mexico sample as L_∞= 388, K= 0.184, and t_0= -1.13. There is little data on the length of the reproductive cycle. Simpfendorfer (1992) stated that the females do not produce a brood each year. Unpublished observations by the authors also suggest a longer than yearly reproductive cycle. The length of the gestation period is also uncertain. Clark and von Schmidt (1965) stated that the gestation period may be "slightly over a year", however, this estimate has not been confirmed, although it is probably correct, given that many large carcharhinid sharks have biennial reproduction and year long gestation periods. The nurseries for the tiger shark appear to be in offshore areas, but they have not been described.

Impact of fisheries: Although tiger sharks are caught in numerous fisheries throughout the world, there is a surprising lack of data on catches or landings.

Status: Category 1. The lack of fisheries data and precise reproductive data prevents us from assigning a higher category.

Ganges shark (*Glyphis gangeticus*)

This is a large shark that inhabits rivers and shallow coastal areas of the Indo-Pacific region, primarily around India (Ganges river). Most of the published accounts of the Ganges shark are believed to be based on bull sharks (Bass *et al.* 1973, Compagno 1984) and there are few authentic records. Even

---

4 Species not included in Compagno 1984.

the known specimens in museums are exceedingly few and usually new-born specimens that date back to the nineteenth century (Compagno 1984). Whether the species has a very restricted habitat, is very scarce, or is extinct, remains uncertain.

Status: Category 1. The species has been said to be of uncertain status or possibly extinct (Compagno 1997). We have no data on past populations and can not establish its presence anywhere now.

Note: River sharks, presumably of the genus *Glyphis*, were recently reported from Borneo (Fowler 1997). Whether they are this species, the closely related speartooth shark, or an undescribed species of *Glyphis* is uncertain.

Speartooth shark (*Glyphis glyphis*)

This is a very rare shark of the Indo-West Pacific region that is said to enter rivers. We have only examined a jaw said to come from a Taiwanese longliner. We have no data on its biology or populations.

Status: Category 1.

Daggernose shark (*Isogomphodon oxyrhynchus*)

This is a little known shark of the shallow coastal waters of the Atlantic coast of South America (Compagno 1984). Almost nothing is known of its habits.

Impact of fisheries: It is occasionally seen in the markets of Trinidad (Castro pers. obs.).

Status: Category 1.

Lemon shark (*Negaprion brevirostris*)

This is a common shark of the American tropics. It inhabits shallow coastal areas, especially around shallow reefs.

Reproductive potential: Lemon sharks mature at about 228 cm TL (Springer 1950b). Brown and Gruber (1988) used tetracycline validated vertebral centra to estimate age at maturity of 11.6 years for males and 12.7 years for females, showing the species to be slow growing and long lived. Brown and Gruber reported the von Bertalanffy parameters as follows: L_∞=317.65 cm, K= 0.057 year^{-1}, and t_0= -2.302. Broods consist of 5-17 young that measure about 64 cm TL at birth (Springer 1950b, Clark and von Schmidt 1965). Its reproductive cycle is biennial (Castro 1993b) and gestation lasts ten months (Springer 1950b) to twelve months (Clark and von Schmidt 1965). Its nurseries are in shallow waters around mangrove islands (Springer 1950b).

Impact of fisheries: Although the lemon shark is often caught throughout its range we have no data on catches or landings.

Status: Category 1.

Blue shark (*Prionace glauca*)

The blue shark is cosmopolitan in tropical, subtropical and temperate waters. It is one of the most common and widest-ranging of sharks. It is a pelagic species that inhabits clear, deep, blue waters, usually in temperatures of 10-20°C, at depths greater than 180 m (Castro 1983). Its migratory patterns are complex and encompass great distances, but are poorly understood. Males and females are known to segregate in many areas (Strasburg 1958, Gubanov and Grigor'yev 1975). Strasburg (1958) showed that blue sharks are most abundant in the Pacific between latitudes of 40°N and 50°N.

Reproductive potential: Although, some authors have examined very large numbers of blue sharks, the data on size at maturity of the blue shark is imprecise. This may be due to poor criteria for maturity, incomplete samples or samples that did not include animals of all sizes, or some peculiarities of the blue shark. Pratt (1979) used different criteria for determining maturity of males and gave a range of 153-183 cm FL for male maturity, but when he used the standard criterion of clasper calcification, he observed that the males reached maturity at 183 cm FL (218 cm TL)[5].

---

5 When reading the blue shark literature, one must be aware of the type of length measurements that different authors use: Suda (1953) used precaudal length (PCL); Pratt (1979) used fork length (FL) and gave a regression to convert it total length (FL= 1.73872 + 0.82995 TL); Nakano (1994) also used precaudal length.

Bigelow and Schroeder (1948) suggested that females mature at 213-243 cm TL. Strasburg (1958) stated that the smallest gravid female seen by him measured 214 cm TL. Nakano (1994) used data from 105 600 blue sharks and stated that females matured between 140 and 160 cm (166 and 191 cm TL, using the regression of Pratt), and that males matured at 130 to 160 cm PCL, based on clasper development. This is probably the most prolific of the larger sharks; broods of 28 to 54 young have been reported often (Bigelow and Schroeder 1948, Pratt 1979), but up to 135 young in a brood have been reported (Gubanov and Grigor'yev 1975). Nakano (1994) observed 669 pregnant females in the North Pacific and stated that the number of embryos ranged from 1 to 62, and the average was 25.6 embryos. Strasburg (1958) gave the birth size as 34-48 cm TL. Suda (1953) examined 115 gravid females from the Pacific Ocean and concluded that gestation lasts 9 months and that birth occurs between December and April. Pratt (1979) examined 19 gravid females from the Atlantic and used data from 23 other Atlantic specimens to arrive at a gestation period of 12 months. Nakano (1994) stated that gestation "lasts about a year" based on length frequency histograms, but did not stated how many gravid animals had been observed nor showed any data. The length of the reproductive cycle is believed to be one year (W. Pratt pers. comm.). Nakano (1994) gave the age at maturity as 4-5 years for males and 5-6 years for females based on "growth equations". According to Cailliet et al. (1983), blue sharks become reproductively mature at 6 or 7 years of age and may reach 20 years based on vertebral ring counts. The nursery areas appear to be in open oceanic waters in the higher latitudes of the range. Strasburg (1958) attributed the higher CPUE in the 30-40^{0}N zone of the Pacific Ocean in summer to the presence of new born blue sharks, and commented on the absence of small blue sharks in the warmer parts of the range. Nakano (1994) also stated that parturition occurred in early summer between latitudes of 30^0 to 40^{0}N of the Pacific Ocean.

Impact of fisheries: Blue sharks are generally finned and discarded by high seas fleets, because of the low value of their flesh which is considered of poor quality for human consumption. Their fins are of low value, but the large quantities collected make up for their low price. The numbers of blue sharks caught yearly must be large, although data on discards and landings of blue sharks throughout the world are very difficult to obtain. Vas (1990) documents the blue shark sport fishery catch at Looe, England. Annual catches steadily declined from over 6 000 fish in the 1960-1961 period to 122 sharks in 1986. In France and Denmark, the blue shark catch increased steadily (Fig. 27) from 4 t in 1978 to 358 t in 1994 (FAO 1998). Rey and Alot (1984) reported that a single Spanish longline vessel caught in five years (1979-1983) 1 833 swordfish (61.28 t) and discarded 2 249 (22.77 t) blue sharks. The Azorean fleet catch in ICES area X increased from 11 t in 1987 to 138 t in 1994 (ICES 1995). In the Nova Scotia/Bay of Fundy region of the Canadian Atlantic, blue sharks landings increased from 8 t in 1990 to 102 t in 1994. Fiji reported to FAO that blue shark fin exports grew from 24 t in 1990 to 65.5 t in 1993, and then decreased to 30 t in 1994. Assuming that the fins are about 0.03% of total landings, the 1993 blue shark landings must have been 2 186 t or over 50 800 sharks. In the US commercial pelagic longline swordfish fishery off the US Atlantic coast, the amount of blue sharks discarded dead increased from 526 t in 1987 to 772 t in 1991, with a yearly average of 13 534 blue sharks or 588 t discarded dead (Cramer 1996b). During that period the CPUE for blue sharks decreased from 6.52 in 1986 to 1.57 in 1995 (Cramer 1996a).

Status: Category 3. Although the blue shark is one of the most abundant large vertebrates in the world, we consider it Category 3 because it is caught in significant numbers in the bycatch of numerous longline fisheries. As other shark stocks have declined, blue sharks are no longer discarded and have become used also for meat in some fisheries.

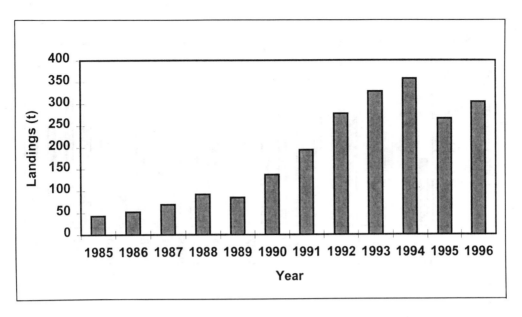

Figure 27. Danish and French blue shark landings from FAO Area 27 (FAO 1996, 1998).

Atlantic sharpnose shark (*Rhizoprionodon terraenovae*)

The Atlantic sharpnose shark is a small coastal carcharhinid. It inhabits the waters of the northeastern coast of North America. It is a common year round resident along the coasts of South Carolinas, Florida and in the Gulf of Mexico. Frequently, the sharks are found in schools of uniform size and sex (Castro 1983).

Reproductive potential: The male sharks mature around 65-80 cm TL and grow to 103 cm TL. The females mature at 85-90 cm TL and reach a length of 110 cm TL. Broods range from 4 to 7 young, which measure 29-32 cm TL (Castro 1983). The mating is in late June with a gestation period about 11-12 months (Castro and Wourms 1993). The von Bertalanffy growth parameter estimates for the species are L_∞= 108 cm, K= 0.359, t_0= -0.985 years. (Branstetter 1987b). Cortés (1995) calculated the population's intrinsic rate of increase was, at best, r= 0.044 year^{-1} (4.5 % year^{-1}).

Impact of fisheries: Large numbers of sharpnose are taken as bycatch in the US shrimp trawling industry. Pellegrin (1996) estimated the bycatch in the shrimp industry in the Gulf of Mexico from 1972 to 1995 (Fig. 28). The Texas Recreational Survey, NMFS Headboat Survey, and the US Marine Recreational Fishing Statistics Survey have estimated a slow increase in the sharpnose fishery. The catch consisted of 43 490 sharpnose sharks in 1981, and the catch rose to 74 876 sharpnose sharks in 1995 (Scott *et al.* 1996).

Status: Category 2. The Atlantic sharpnose is a fast-growing species that reproduces yearly. In spite of being targeted by recreational fisheries, and of the large bycatch in the shrimp industry, the populations seem to be maintaining themselves readily in the Gulf of Mexico.

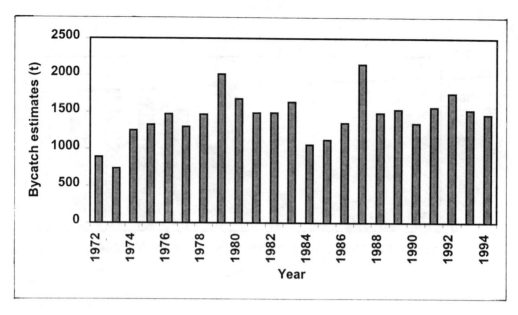

Figure 28. Bycatch estimates for sharpnose sharks, United States Gulf of Mexico, 1972-94 (Pellegrin 1996).

4.2.30 Hammerhead sharks, Family Sphyrnidae

The flat, wide, hammer or shovel-shaped head of these sharks is so characteristic that they can not be confused with any other sharks. They are small to large sharks of the coastal areas of tropical and warm-temperate seas. Some are widely distributed.

Winghead shark (*Eusphyra blochii*)

This is a poorly known hammerhead shark of the tropical Indo-West Pacific area. It is found in shallow water of the continental and insular shelves (Compagno 1984).

Reproductive potential: Males mature at about 108 cm TL and females at about 120 cm TL. The young measure about 45-50 cm TL at birth, and broods range from 6 to 25 young, with a mean of 12. The gestation period is believed to be about 10-11 months, and the reproductive cycle is annual (Stevens and Lyle 1989).

Impact of fisheries: The species is said to be common in the fisheries of India, Pakistan, Malaysia, and Thailand by Compagno (1984), but we have no fisheries data.

Status: Category 1.

Scalloped bonnethead (*Sphyrna corona*)

This is a little known hammerhead of the eastern tropical Pacific.

Status: Category 1.

Whitefin hammerhead (*Sphyrna couardi*)

This is poorly known hammerhead of the African coast.

Status: Category 1.

Scalloped hammerhead (*Sphyrna lewini*)

This is a very common, large, schooling hammerhead of warm waters. It is the commonest hammerhead in the tropics and is readily available in abundance to inshore artisanal and small commercial fisheries as well as offshore operations (Compagno 1984).

Reproductive potential: Males in the Atlantic mature at about 180-185 cm TL (Bigelow and Schroeder 1948) and in the Indian Ocean at 140-165 cm TL (Bass *et al.* 1973). Females mature about 200 cm TL (Stevens and Lyle 1989). The young are born at 38-45 cm TL, and broods consist of 15-31 young

(Compagno 1984). The reproductive cycle is annual (Castro 1993b) and the gestation period is 9-10 months (Stevens and Lyle 1989). The nurseries are in shallow coastal waters (Castro 1993b).

Impact of fisheries: Because the scalloped hammerhead forms very large schools in coastal areas, it is targeted by many fisheries for their high-priced fins. Ulrich (1996) reported that in his independent fishery monitoring of large coastal sharks off South Carolina, the catch of this species declined from 3% in 1983-84 to 1% in 1994-95. The USA data for the scalloped hammerhead is often combined with two other species, the great and smooth hammerheads. The scalloped hammerhead is by far the most abundant of the three species, so the data probably reflects best the condition of scalloped hammerhead stocks. Cramer (1996a) reported that the CPUE index for hammerheads in the US Atlantic fisheries fell from 2.9 in 1986 to 0.64 in 1995 (Fig. 29). Scott (1996) showed a decline in CPUE (Fig. 30) for hammerheads in the US Gulf of Mexico, party boat fishery.

Status: Category 3. We consider the scalloped hammerhead Category 3, because its schooling habit makes it extremely vulnerable to gillnet fisheries, and because scalloped hammerheads are actively pursued in many fisheries throughout the world, and they are easily caught in very large numbers.

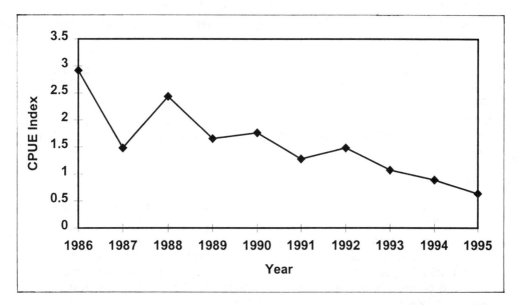

Figure 29. CPUE series for hammerheads from pelagic fishery logbooks, US Atlantic coast (Cramer 1996a).

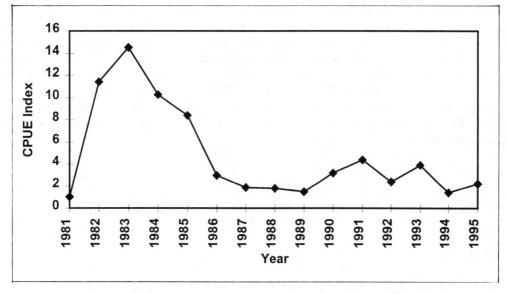

Figure 30. CPUE series for hammerheads in the US Gulf of Mexico, party boat fishery (Scott 1996).

Scoophead (*Sphyrna media*)

This is a little known, small hammerhead of the American tropics.

Status: Category 1.

Great hammerhead (*Sphyrna mokarran*)

This is a large shark found both in open oceans and shallow coastal waters. It is circumtropical in warm waters (Castro 1983). It is one of the largest sharks. It is usually a solitary fish, unlike the more common scalloped hammerhead that often forms very large schools.

Reproductive potential: In Australia males mature at about 225 cm TL and females at 210 cm TL (Stevens and Lyle 1989).Young measure about 67 cm TL at birth (Stevens and Lyle 1989) and broods consist of 20-40 young (Castro 1983). The gestation period lasts about 11 months (Stevens and Lyle 1989). The reproductive cycle is biennial (Stevens and Lyle 1989).

Impact of fisheries: Great hammerheads are caught in coastal longline shark fisheries as well as in pelagic tuna and swordfish longlines. Berkeley and Campos (1988) stated that great hammerheads constituted 0.7% of all sharks caught in swordfish longlines off Florida. Its fins bring the highest prices in the fin market. In many fishing operations, the fins are removed while the carcasses are discarded at sea. Landings of great hammerheads are usually lumped together with those of the scalloped hammerhead.

Status: Category 3. We consider the great hammerhead to be Category 3, because of its biennial reproductive cycle, and because it is caught both in directed fisheries and as bycatch in tuna and swordfish fisheries.

Bonnethead (*Sphyrna tiburo*)

The bonnethead is a small hammerhead that inhabits shallow coastal waters where it frequents sandy or muddy bottoms. It is confined to the warm waters of the American continent (Castro 1983).

Reproductive potential: Males mature at about 70 cm TL, females mature at about 85 cm TL (Parsons 1993). The young measure 27-35 cm TL at birth and broods consist of 8-12 young (Castro 1983, Parsons 1993). Parsons (1993) estimated the gestation period of two Florida populations at 4.5-5 months, one of the shortest gestation periods known for sharks. The reproductive cycle is annual (Castro pers. obs.).

Impact of fisheries: The only data that we have on bonnethead catches is for the United States. In the US Gulf of Mexico, shrimp trawl bycatch from 1972-94 (Fig. 31) remained stable over that period (Pellegrin 1996).

Status: Category 2. We consider the species to be of lesser risk, because it is a fast growing species that reproduces annually, and more importantly, because it is generally not targeted by commercial fisheries due to its small size. Although some bonnetheads are caught as bycatch in gillnet fisheries operating in shallow waters of the southeastern United States, these net fisheries are slowly being outlawed by the various states. The resiliency of the bonnethead is evidenced by the shrimp trawl bycatch in the US Gulf of Mexico which has remained stable over twenty years.

In the United States, the bonnethead is classified as a "small coastal shark" in the Fishery Management Plan for Sharks of the Atlantic Ocean of the United States, for which there are no catch or landings quota or limit.

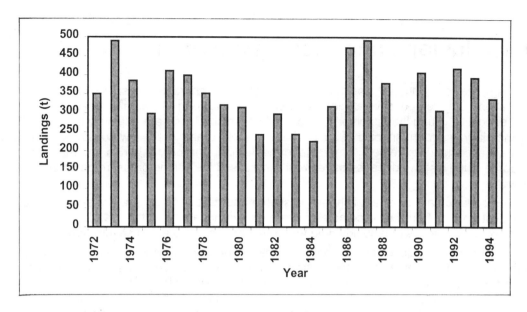

Figure 31. Shrimp trawl bycatch of the bonnethead in the US Gulf of Mexico (Pellegrin 1996).

Smalleye hammerhead (*Sphyrna tudes*)

The smalleye or golden hammerhead is a poorly known species that inhabits the northeastern coast of South America from Venezuela to Uruguay. It is found in coastal waters at depths of 9-40 m over muddy bottoms. It is a small species that attains a maximum size of 122 cm TL and 9 kg (Castro 1989).

Reproductive potential: Males mature at about 80 cm TL and females mature at about 98 cm TL. The young measure about 30 cm TL at birth and broods consist of 5 to 12 young. The gestation cycle lasts about 10 months and the reproductive cycle is annual. The nurseries are in shallow muddy beaches (Castro 1989).

Impact of fisheries: Although the smalleye hammerhead is captured in many artisanal fisheries throughout its range, there is no published information on catches, except for a brief mention of catches off the Guianas by Kleijn (1974). The senior author observed large catches of this species in gillnet fisheries along the northeastern coast of Trinidad in 1985-86. Gillnets were seen to be very effective in catching even the smallest hammerheads. Upon return to the same area a decade later, only a handful of smalleye hammerheads were caught in the course of a week's fishing. It appeared that the unrestricted gillnet fishery had heavily reduced the local population of smalleye hammerheads.

Status: Category 3. We consider the species Category 3 because of its limited reproductive potential and because its habitat and nurseries are in shallow coastal waters, where it is caught by artisanal gillnet fisheries.

Smooth hammerhead (*Sphyrna zygaena*)

This is a common hammerhead of temperate waters. Fisheries data for hammerheads includes this species and the scalloped and great hammerheads.

Status: Category 1. See the status for the scalloped hammerhead.

5. Conclusions and recommendations

1. Sharks have an unusual combination of biological characteristics: slow growth, delayed maturation, long reproductive cycles, low fecundity and long life spans. Sharks produce small numbers of live young that hatch or are born fully developed, and are relatively large at birth. Many commercially important species of sharks have nursery areas in shallow coastal waters. All these factors make sharks extremely vulnerable to overfishing. The new fisheries and markets that have appeared in the last two decades have greatly increased the fishing pressure on sharks throughout the world.

2. Species specific data on shark fisheries is scarce and difficult to obtain. Consequently, our report is modest and far from being complete. However, we have shown that nearly all the species for which we have catches or landings data for more than ten years are in severe declines.

   The documented declines are probably indicative of what is happening to many species in undocumented fisheries. For example, the thresher shark population has declined severely off the western coast of the United States. Because the thresher is also being fished in the Atlantic by several nations, it is likely that Atlantic populations have suffered similar but undocumented declines. Our evaluations can only confirm Holden's (1968) observation that most elasmobranch fisheries collapse following initial exploitation.

3. Concerns about overfishing and the collapse of shark stocks have engendered worldwide attempts to manage and conserve sharks. If these attempts at management and conservation of sharks are to be successful, we must do the following:

   a) We need to better understand the shark fisheries and their effects. Efforts must be made to collect species specific data on the shark fisheries. These efforts must be directed to the lowest data collection levels by fishery workers. It will take a concerted effort by interested agencies and countries to improve the training of fishery workers in shark identification before meaningful statistics from shark fisheries can be expected. In the authors' experience, this can be done by training programmes and the use of simple, inexpensive regional guides to the species found in local fisheries.

   b) A conservation ethic for sharks must be developed. Educational programmes that explain the role of sharks in the ocean, the value of sharks as a resource, and their vulnerability to overfishing, may be one of the cheapest and most effective methods to promote the rational and sustainable use of natural resources. The attitude that sharks are man's "competitors that reduce the abundance of certain valuable resources" (Taniuchi 1990), is still common. Educational programmes must be directed at the public as well as to fishery managers. Fishery managers must be made aware that sharks do not support intensive fisheries, so that they can prevent the unregulated development and irrational overexploitation of shark fisheries.

   c) Shark fisheries need to be managed to ensure their long-term conservation and sustainable use (see FAO Code of Conduct for Responsible Fisheries, paragraph 7.1). Levels of fishing effort should be commensurate with the low reproductive capacity of these species (CoC 7.1.8). Appropriate measures should be taken to minimise shark discards (CoC 7.6.9). Timely, complete and reliable statistics on catch and fishing effort should be maintained and disseminated (CoC 7.4.4).

This may require international agreements among concerned nations and reductions in catches and bycatch. Given the current, worldwide interest in the short-term exploitation of sharks for fins and meat, attempts at the protection of shark stocks are likely to be difficult. Unless efforts are undertaken promptly to reduce present catch rates and bycatch, the future of the shark resources is very bleak.

6. References

Aasen, O. 1963. Length and growth of the porbeagle [*Lamna nasus* (Bonnaterre)] in the North West Atlantic. *Fiskerdir. Skr. Ser. Havunders* 13(6): 20-37.

Ackerman, L.T. 1971. Contributions to the biology of the leopard shark, *Triakis semifasciata* (Girard) in Elkhorn Slough, Monterey Bay, California. M.A. Thesis, Sacramento State College, Sacramento. 54 pp.

Amorim, A.F. & C.A. Arfelli. 1993. Status of shark species off the Brazilian coast. In Fourth Indo-Pacific Fish Conference, Bangkok, Thailand, Programs and Abstracts of Papers, Bangkok. 64 pp.

Anderson, R.C. & H. Ahmed. 1993. *The shark fisheries of the Maldives*. Ministry of Fisheries and Agriculture, Maldives. FAO, Madras. 76 pp.

Backus, R.H., S. Springer, and E.L. Arnold, Jr. 1956. A contribution to the natural history of the white-tip shark, *Pterolamiops longimanus* (Poey). *Deep-Sea Res.* 3: 178-188.

Bass, A.J. 1970. Shark distribution and movements along the eastern coast of South Africa. *Oceanogr. Res. Inst. (Durban).* Paper G5. 13 pp.

Bass, A.J., J.D. D' Aubrey & N. Kistnasamy. 1973. Sharks of the east coast of southern Africa. I. The genus *Carcharhinus* (Carcharhinidae). *Oceanogr. Res. Inst. (Durban) Investig. Rep.* 33: 168 pp.

Beamish, R.J. & G.A. McFarlane. 1983. The forgotten requirement for age validation in fisheries biology. *Trans. Am. Fish. Soc.* 112 (6): 735-743.

Beamish, R.J. & G.A. McFarlane. 1985. Annulus development on the second dorsal spine of the spiny dogfish (Squalus acanthias) and its validity for age determination. *Can. J. Fish. Aquat. Sci.* 42: 1799-1805.

Bedford, D.W. 1985. Pelagic shark/swordfish drift gill net fishery. Calif. Dept. Fish. Game, Management Information Document. 74pp.

Bedford, D.W. 1987. Shark management: A case history- the California pelagic shark and swordfish fishery. *In* S. Cook ed. *Sharks: an inquiry into biology, behavior, fisheries, and use.* Portland, Oregon State Univ. Extension Service, Portland. pp. 161-171.

Beebe, W. & J. Tee-Van. 1941. Eastern Pacific expeditions of the New York Zoological Society. 25. Fishes from the tropical eastern Pacific. Part.2. Sharks. *Zoologica (N.Y.)* 26: 93-122.

Berkeley, S.A. & W.L. Campos. 1988. Relative abundance and fishery potential of pelagic sharks along Florida's east coast. *Mar. Fish. Rev.* 50 (1): 9-16.

Bigelow, H.B. & W.C. Schroeder. 1948. Fishes of the western North Atlantic. Part.1. Lancelets, cyclostomes and sharks. New Haven: Mem. Sears Fdn. Mar. Res. 576 pp.

Bjerkan, P. & E. Koefoed. 1957. Notes on the Greenland shark, *Acanthorhinus carcharias* (Gunn). *Fiskeridir. Skr. Ser. Havunders* 11(10): 1-12.

Blagoderov, A.I. 1994. Seasonal distribution and some notes on the biology of salmon shark (Lamna ditropis) in the northwestern Pacific Ocean. *J. Ichthyol.* 34(2): 115- 121.

Bonfil, R. 1994. Overview of world elasmobranch fisheries. *FAO Fish. Tech. Pap.*, 341, 119 pp.

Bonfil, R., R. Mena & D. de Anda. 1993. Biological parameters of commercially exploited silky sharks, *Carcharhinus falciformis*, from the Campeche Bank, Mexico. *In* S. Branstetter ed. *Conservation Biology of Sharks.* NOAA Technical Report NMFS 115. U.S. Dept. Comm., Miami. 14 pp.

Brander, K. 1981. Disappearance of common skate *Raia batis* from Irish Sea. *Nature* 290: 48-49.

Branstetter, S. 1987a. Age and growth estimates for blacktip, *Carcharhinus limbatus*, and spinner, *Carcharhinus brevipinna*, sharks from the Northwestern Gulf of Mexico. *Copeia* 1987: 964-974.

Branstetter, S. 1987b. Age and growth validation of newborn sharks held in laboratory aquaria, with comments on the life history of the Atlantic sharpnose shark, *Rhizoprionodon terraenovae*. *Copeia* 1987: 219-300.

Branstetter, S. 1990. Early life history implications of selected carcharhinoid and lamnoid sharks of the Northwest Atlantic. *In* H.L. Pratt, S. Gruber & T. Taniuchi eds. *Elasmobranchs as living resources: Advances in the biology, ecology, systematics, and the status of the fisheries.* NOAA Technical Report NMFS 90. U.S. Dept. Comm., Washington DC: 17-28.

Branstetter, S. & J.D. McEachran. 1986. Age and growth of four carcharhinid sharks common to the Gulf of Mexico: A summary paper. *In* T. Uyeno, R. Arai, T. Taniuchi & K. Matsuura, eds. *Indo-Pacific Fish Biology: Proceedings of the Second International Conference on Indo-Pacific Fishes.* Ichthyol. Soc. Japan. pp. 361-371.

Branstetter, S. & J.A. Musick. 1994. Age and growth estimates for the sand tiger in the northwestern Atlantic Ocean. *Trans. Am. Fish. Soc.* 123: 242-254.

Branstetter, S., J.A. Musick & J.A. Colvocoresses. 1987. A comparison of the age and growth of the tiger shark, *Galeocerdo cuvieri*, from off Virginia and from the northwestern Gulf of Mexico. *Fishery Bulletin* 85: 269-279.

Branstetter, S. & R. Stiles. 1987. Age and growth estimates of the bull shark, *Carcharhinus leucas*, from the northern Gulf of Mexico. *Environ. Biol. Fishes* 20(3): 169-181.

Brown, C.A. 1996. Standardized catch rates of four shark species in the Virginia-Massachusetts (U.S.) rod and reel fishery 1986-1995. Document SB-III-2. 1996 Shark Stock Assessment Workshop. NOAA/NMFS/SEFSC, Miami. 9 pp.

Brown, C.A. & S.H. Gruber. 1988. Age assessment of the lemon shark, *Negaprion brevirostris*, using tetracycline validated vertebral centra. *Copeia* 1988: 747- 753.

Cadenat, J. & J. Blache. 1981. Requins de Méditerranée et d' Atlantique. Faune Trop.ORSTOM 21: 330 pp.

Cailliet, G.M. 1992. Demography of the Central California population of the leopard shark (*Triakis semifasciata*). *Aust. J. Mar. Freshw. Res.* 43:183-193.

Cailliet, G.M. & D.W. Bedford. 1983. The biology of three pelagic sharks from California waters, and their emerging fisheries: A review. *California Mar. Res. Comm.*, COFI Rep. 24: 57-69.

Cailliet, G.M., L.K. Martin, J.T. Harvey, D. Kusher & B.A. Welden. 1983. Preliminary studies on the age and growth of blue, Prionace glauca, common thresher, *Alopias vulpinus*, and shortfin mako, *Isurus oxyrhinchus*, sharks from California waters. NOAA Technical Report NMFS 8. U.S. Dept. Comm., Washington DC. pp 179-188.

Cailliet, G.M., L.J. Natanson, B.A. Welden & D.A. Ebert. 1985. Preliminary studies on the age and growth of the white shark, Carcharodon carcharias, using vertebral bands. *Mem. South. Calif. Acad. Sci.* 9: 49-60.

Cailliet, G.M., R.L. Radke & B.A. Welden. 1986. Elasmobranch age determination and verification: A review. *In* T. Uyeno, R. Arai, T. Taniuchi & K. Matsuura, eds. *Indo-Pacific Fish Biology: Proceedings of the second international conference on Indo-Pacific fishes.* Ichthyol. Soc. Japan., Tokyo. pp 345-360.

Cailliet, G.M., D.B. Holts & D. Bedford. 1991. A review of the commercial fisheries for sharks on the west coast of the United States. *In* J. Pepperell, J. West & P.Woon, eds. *Shark conservation: Proceedings of an international workshop on the conservation of elasmobranchs.* Taronga Zoo, Sydney. pp 13-29.

Cailliet, G.M., H.F. Mollet, G.G. Pittenger, D Bedford & L.J. Natanson. 1992. Growth and demography of the Pacific angel shark, (*Squatina californica*), based upon tag returns off California. *Aust. J. Mar. Freshwater Res.* 43: 1313-1330.

Casey, J.G., F.J. Mather, III, J.M. Mason, Jr. & J. Hoenig. 1978. Offshore fisheries of the middle Atlantic Bight. *Mar. Rec. Fish.* 3: 107-129.

Casey, J.G. & N.E. Kohler. 1992. Tagging studies on the shortfin mako shark (*Isurus oxyrhinchus*) in the western North Atlantic. *Aust. J. Mar. Freshwater Res.* 43: 45- 60.

Casey, J.G. & L.J. Natanson. 1992. Revised estimates of age and growth of the sandbar shark (Carcharhinus plumbeus) from the western North Atlantic. *Can. J. Fish. Aquat. Sci.* 49(7): 1474-1477.

Castillo, G.J.L. 1992. Diagnostico de la pesquería de tiburón en México. Secretaría de Pesca, México. 72pp.

Castro, J.I. 1983. The sharks of North American waters. Tex. A&M Univ. Press, College Station. 180 pp.

Castro, J.I. 1987. The importance of sharks in marine biological communities. *In* S. Cook, ed. *Sharks: An inquiry into biology, behavior, fisheries, and use.* Oregon State University Extension Service, Portland. pp 11-18.

Castro, J.I. 1989: The biology of the golden hammerhead, *Sphyrna tudes*, off Trinidad. *Environ. Biol. Fishes* 24(1): 3-11.

Castro, J.I. 1993a. The biology of the finetooth shark, *Carcharhinus isodon. Environ. Biol. Fishes* 36: 219-232.

Castro, J.I. 1993b. The shark nursery of Bulls Bay, South Carolina, with a review of the shark nurseries of the southeastern coast of the United States. *Environ. Biol. Fishes* 38 (1): 37-48.

Castro, J.I. 1996. The biology of the blacktip shark, *Carcharhinus limbatus*, off the southeastern United States. *Bull. Mar. Sci.* 59 (3): 508-522.

Castro, J.I. & J.P. Wourms. 1993. Reproduction, placentation, and embryonic development of the Atlantic sharpnose shark, *Rhizoprionodon terraenovae. J. Morph.* 218: 257-280.

Chen, C-T, K-M Liu & Y-C Chang. 1997. Reproductive biology of the bigeye thresher shark, *Alopias superciliosus*, (Lowe, 1839) (Chondrichthyes: Alopiidae), in the northwestern Pacific. *Ichthyol. Res.* 44:227-235.

Chute, G.R. 1930. The lily-iron returns to Monterey Bay: shark fishing recommences on a harpoon basis. *Calif. Fish. Game* 16 (2): 143-152.

Clark, A.H. 1887. The whale fishery: history and present condition of the fishery. *In* G. B. Goode, ed. *The fisheries and fishery industries of the United States, Section 5, History and methods of the fisheries.* Vol. 2. U.S. Govt. Printing Off Washington. pp. 3-329.

Clark, E. 1963. The maintenance of sharks in captivity, with a report of their instrumental conditioning. *In* P. Gilbert, ed. *Sharks and survival.* D.C. Heath and Co., Boston. pp. 115-149.

Clark, E. & K. von Schmidt. 1965. Sharks of the central gulf coast of Florida. *Bull. Mar. Sci.* 15: 13-83.

Cliff, G. & S.F.J. Dudley. 1992. Sharks caught in the protective gill nets off Natal, South Africa. 6. The copper shark Carcharhinus brachyurus (Günther). *S. Afr. J. Mar. Sci.* 12: 663-674.

Compagno, L.J.V. 1984. FAO Species Catalogue Vol. 4, Part 1 and 2: Sharks of the world: An annotated and illustrated catalogue of shark species known to date. FAO Fish. Synop. 125. FAO, Rome, Italy.

Compagno, L.J.V. 1991. Government protection for the great white shark (*Carcharodon carcharias*) in South Africa. *S. Afr. J. Mar. Sci.* 87: 284-285.

Compagno, L.J.V. 1997. Threatened fishes of the world: *Glyphis gangeticus* (Müller & Henle, 1839) (Carcharhinidae). *Environ. Biol. Fish.* 49: 400.

Cook, S. 1990. Trends in shark fin markets: 1980s, 1990s and beyond. *Chondros*, 15 March: 3-5

Cortés, E. 1995. Demographic analysis of the Atlantic sharpnose shark, *Rhizoprionodon terraenovae*, in the Gulf of Mexico. *U.S. Fish Wildl. Serv. Fish. Bull.* 93: 57-66.

Cramer, J. 1996a. Large pelagic logbook indices for sharks. Document SB-III-3. 1996 Shark Stock Assessment Workshop. NOAA/NMFS/SEFSC, Miami. 7 pp.

Cramer, J. 1996b. Estimates of the numbers and metric tons of sharks discarded dead by pelagic longline vessels. Document SB-III-4. 1996 Shark Stock Assessment Workshop. NOAA/NMFS/SEFSC, Miami. 21 pp.

CSIRO, Division of Fisheries Research. 1990. Analysis of Taiwanese gill-net fishery: Final report to the Fishing Industry Research and Development Council (Project 87/19). 93 pp.

da Silva, H. M. 1983. Preliminary studies of the exploited stock of kitefin shark, *Scymnorhinus licha* (Bonnaterre 1788) in the Azores. International Council for the Exploration of the Sea, Demersal Fish Committee cm1983/g:18. 18pp.

da Silva, H. M. 1987. An assessment of the Azorean stock of kitefin shark, *Dalatias licha* (Bonn 1788). ICES, Demersal Fish Committee cm 1987/g:66. 11pp.

da Silva, H. M. 1988. Growth and reproduction of kitefin shark, *Dalatias licha* (Bonn 1788) in Azorean waters. ICES, Demersal Fish Committee cm 1988/g:21. 16pp.

Davenport, S. & J.D. Stevens. 1988. Age and growth of two commercially important sharks from Northern Australia. *Austr. J. Mar. Freshw. Res.* 39: 417-433.

Dodrill, J.W. 1977. A hook and line survey of the sharks found within five hundred meters of shore along Melbourne Beach, Brevard County, Florida. M.S. Thesis. Florida Inst. Tech., Melbourne, Florida. 304 pp.

Dudley, S.F.J. & G. Cliff. 1993. Sharks caught in the protective gills nets off Natal, South Africa. 7. The blacktip shark Carcharhinus limbatus (Valenciennes). *S. Afr. J. Mar. Sci.* 13: 237-254.

Ebert, D.A. 1986. Observations on the elasmobranch assemblage of San Francisco Bay. *Calif. Dep. Fish. Game. Fish. Bull.* 72(4): 244-249.

Ebert, D.A. 1989. Life history of the sevengill shark, Notorynchus cepedianus Peron, in two northern California bays. *Calif. Dep. Fish. Game. Fish. Bull.* 75(2): 102-112.

FAO. 1996. FAO yearbook: Fishery statistics: Catches and landings. FAO Fisheries Series No. 46., Vol. 78. 700 pp.

FAO. 1998. FAO yearbook: Fishery statistics: Capture production. FAO Fisheries Series No. 50., Vol. 82. 678 pp.

Ficher, N.S. 1996. Pesca e avaliação da mortalidade total sobre a população de *Mustelus schmitti* (Springer 1940) (Triakidae, carcharhiniformes) na plataforma continetal do Rio Grande do Sul. Tese de Maestrado. Departamento de Oceanografia. Fundação Universidade do Rio Grande. Rio Grande, Brazil. 71 pp.

Fitch, J.E. 1948. Use of DUKW's in the fishery for basking sharks, *Cetorhinus maximus. Calif. Dep. Fish. Game, Fish. Bull.* 34(4): 219-220.

Ford, E. 1921. A contribution to our knowledge of the life histories of the dogfishes landed at Plymouth. *J. Mar. Biol. Ass.* U.K. 12: 468-505.

Fourmanoir, P. 1961. Requins de la côte ouest de Madagascar. Memoires de L'Institut Scientifique de Madagascar. Tome IV. 81 pp.

Fowler, S. 1997. River shark discovered in Sabah. Shark News (Newsletter of the IUCN Shark Specialist Group) 9:11

Francis, M.P. 1996. Observations on a pregnant white shark with a review of reproductive biology. *In* A.P. Klimley & D.G. Ainley, eds. *Great white sharks: The biology of Carcharodon carcharias.* Academic Press, New York. pp.157-172.

Frej, L. & A.-C. Gustaffsson. 1990. The market for shark and shark products in southern India. Fisheries Development Series 48. ISSN 0280-5375. Bay of Bengal Program, Madras. 49 pp.

Garrick, J.A.F. 1982. Sharks of the genus Carcharhinus. NOAA Technical Report NMFS Circ. 445. U.S. Dept. Comm., Washington DC. 194 pp.

Gauld, J.A. 1989. Records of porbeagles landed in Scotland, with observations on the biology, distribution and exploitation of the species. Scottish Fisheries Research Report 45. Dept. Agriculture and Fisheries for Scotland, Edinburgh. 15 pp.

Gilmore, R.G., J.W. Dodrill & P.A. Lindley. 1983. Reproduction and embryonic development of the sand tiger shark, *Odontaspis taurus* (Rafinesque). *U.S. Fish Wildl. Serv. Fish Bull.* 81 (2): 201-225.

Govender, A., N. Kistnasamy & R.P. Van Der Elst. 1991. Growth of spotted ragged- tooth sharks, *Carcharias taurus* (Rafinesque) in captivity. *S. Afr. J. Mar. Sci.* 11: 15-19.

Gubanov, Y.P. 1978. The reproduction of some species of pelagic sharks from the equatorial zone of the Indian Ocean. *J. Ichth.* 18: 781-792.

Gubanov, Y.P. & V.N. Grigor'yev. 1975. Observations on the distribution and biology of the blue shark Prionace glauca (Carcharinidae) of the Indian Ocean. *J. Ichth.* 15: 37-43.

Guitart Manday, D. 1975. Las pesquerias pelágico-oceanicas de corto radio de acción en la región noroccidental de Cuba. Academia de Ciencias de Cuba, Instituto de Oceanología. *Serie Oceanología* 31. 26 pp.

Hanan, D.A. 1984. Analysis of the common thresher shark, Alopias vulpinus, in the California Bight. NOAA/NMFS/SWFSC Admin. Rep. LJ-84-10C. 34 pp.

Hanan, D.A., D.B. Holts & A.L. Coan, Jr. 1993. The California drift net fishery for sharks and swordfish, 1981-82 through 1990-91. *Calif. Dept. Fish. Game. Fish Bull.* 175. 95 pp.

Hansen, P.M. 1963. Tagging experiments with the Greenland shark [*Somniosus microcephalus* (Bloch and Schneider)] in subarea 1. *Int. Comm. Northwest Atl. Fish. Spec. Publ.* 4: 172-175.

Harvey-Clark, C. 1995. Protection of sixgill sharks. *In* N.L. Shackell & J.H.M. Willison, ed. *Marine protected areas and sustainable fisheries.* Sci. Manag. Protected Areas Ass., Nova Scotia. pp. 286-289.

Herald, E.S. 1968. Size and aggressiveness of the sevengill shark (*Notorynchus maculatus*). *Copeia* 1968: 412-444.

Hisaw, F.L. & A. Albert. 1947. Observations on the reproduction of the spiny dogfish, *Squalus acanthias*. *Biol. Bull. (Woods Hole)* 92: 187-199.

Hoff, T.B. 1990. Conservation and management of the western North Atlantic shark resource based on the life history strategy limitations of sandbar sharks. Ph.D. dissertation, Univ. of Delaware. 282 pp.

Holden, M.J. 1968. The rational exploitation of the Scottish-Norwegian stocks of spurdogs (*Squalus acanthias* L.). *Fish. Invest.* 25(8). Ministry of Agriculture, Fish. Food, London. 28 pp.

Holden, M.J. 1974. Problems in the rational exploitation of elasmobranch populations and some suggested solutions. *In* F.R.Harden Jones, ed. *Sea Fisheries Research*. J. Wiley and Sons, New York. pp. 117-137.

Holts, D.B. 1988. Review of U.S. west coast commercial shark fisheries. *U.S. Natl. Mar. Fish. Serv. Mar. Fish. Rev.* 50(1): 1-8.

Holts, D.B., A. Julian, O. Sosa-Nishizaki & N.W. Bartoo. 1996. Pelagic shark fisheries along the west coast of the United States and Baja California, Mexico. *American Fisheries Society 1995 Proceedings*. 37 pp.

Hueter, R.E. 1991. Survey of the Florida recreational shark fishery utilizing shark tournament and selected longline data. Final report, Florida Dept. Nat. Res. grant agreement 6627. Mote Marine Laboratory, Sarasota. 74 pp.

ICES. 1995. Report of the study group on elasmobranch fishes. ICES cm 1995/g:3. ICES Headquarters, Copenhagen. 92 pp.

Jensen, A.C. 1966. Life history of the spiny dogfish. *U.S. Fish Wildl. Serv. Fish. Bull.* 65: 527-554.

Jensen, A.S. 1914. The selachians of Greenland. Mindeskrift for Japetus Steenstrupp. B. L. Bogtrykkeri, Copenhagen. 40 pp.

Jensen, N.H. 1976. Reproduction of the bull shark *Carcharhinus leucas*, in the Lake Nicaragua-Rio San Juan system. *In* T. B. Thorson, ed. *Investigations of the ichthyofauna of Nicaraguan lakes*. University of Nebraska-Lincoln, Lincoln. pp. 539-559.

Jones, B.C. & G.H. Geen. 1977. Morphometric changes in an elasmobranch *Squalus acanthias* after preservation. *Can. J. Zool.* 55: 1060-1062.

Joung, S.J., C-T Chen, E. Clark, S. Uchida & W.Y.P. Huang. 1996. The whale shark, *Rhincodon typus*, is a livebearer: 300 embryos found in a one "Megamamma" supreme. *Environ. Biol. Fishes* 46: 219-223.

Kleijn, L.J.K. 1974. Results of experimental and exploratory fishing off northeastern South America (MFR paper 1089). *Mar. Fish. Rev.* 36 (9): 67-77.

Krefft, G. & E. Tortonese. 1973. Squalidae. In check list of the fishes of the north- eastern Atlantic and of the Mediterranean. *UNESCO 1*: 46.

Kunzlik, P.A. 1988. The basking shark. Dept. of Agriculture and Fisheries for Scotland. Scottish Fisheries Information Pamphlet 14. 21 pp.

Kusher, D.I., S.E. Smith & G.M. Cailliet. 1992. Validated age and growth of the leopard shark (*Triakis semifasciata*) with comments on reproduction. *Environ. Biol. Fishes* 35: 187-203.

Last, P.R. & J.D. Stevens. 1994. Sharks and rays of Australia. CSIRO, Australia. 512 pp.

Liu, K-M, P-J Chiang & C-T Chen, 1998. Age and growth estimates of the bigeye thresher shark, *Alopias superciliosus*, in northeastern Taiwan waters. *U.S. Fish Wildl. Serv. Fish. Bull.* 96: 482-491.

Lyle, J.M. 1987. Northern pelagic fish stock research programme: summary of catch and effort data. Dept. of Industries and Development, Northern Territory. Fish. Rep. 16. 54 pp.

Martinez, J.L. 1947. The Cuban shark industry. U.S. Fish Widl. Serv. Fishery Leaflet 250. 18 pp.

Menni, R.C. 1986. Shark biology in Argentina: A review. *In* T. Uyeno, T. Arai, T. Taniuchi & K. Matsuura, ed. *Indo-Pacific fish biology*: Proceedings of the Second International Conference, on Indo-Pacific fishes. Tokyo, Ichthyological Society of Japan, pp. 425-436.

Miller, D.J. & R.N. Lea. 1972. Guide to the coastal marine fishes of California. *Calf. Dept. Fish. Game, Fish. Bull.* 157. 235 pp.

Moreno, J.A. & J. Morón. 1992. Reproductive biology of the bigeye thresher shark, *Alopias superciliosus* (Lowe 1839). *Aust. J. Mar. Freshwater Res.* 43: 77-86.

Moulton, P.L., T.I. Walker & S.R. Saddlier. 1992. Age and growth studies of gummy shark, *Mustelus antarcticus* Günther, and school shark, *Galeorhinus galeus* (Linnaeus), from southern Australian waters. *Aust. J. Mar. Freshwater Res.* 43: 1241-1267.

Muñoz-Chapuli, R., G. Notarbartolo di Sciara, B. Séret & M. Stehmann. 1993. The status of the elasmobranch fisheries in Europe. Report of the Northeast Atlantic subgroup of the IUCN Shark Specialist Group. 23 pp.

Musick, J.A., S. Branstetter & J.A. Colvocoresses. 1993. Trends in shark abundance from 1974 to 1991 for the Chesapeake Bight region of the U.S. Mid-Atlantic Coast. *In* S. Branstetter, ed. *Conservation biology of elasmobranchs*. NOAA Technical Report NMFS 115: 1-18.

Nakamura, H. 1935. On the two species of the thresher shark from Formosan waters. Mem. Fac. Sci. Agric. Taihoku Imp. Univ. 14: 1-6.

Nakano, H. 1994. Age, reproduction and migration of blue shark in the North Pacific Ocean. *Bull. Nat. Inst. Far Seas Fish.* 31: 141-144.

Nammack, M.F., J.A. Musick & J.A. Colvocoresses. 1985. Life history of spiny dogfish off the northeastern United States. *Trans. Am. Fish. Soc.* 114: 367-376.

Natanson, L.J. & G.M. Cailliet. 1990. Vertebral growth zone deposition in Pacific angel sharks. *Copeia* 1990: 1133-1145.

Natanson, L.J., J.G. Casey & N.E. Kohler. 1995. Age and growth estimates for the dusky shark, Carcharhinus obscurus, in the western North Atlantic Ocean. *U.S. Fish Wildl. Serv. Fish. Bull.* 93: 116-126.

NEFSC. 1994. Report of the 18th Northeast Regional Stock Assessment Workshop: Stock Assessment Review Committee, Consensus Summary Assessments. NOAA/NMFS/NEFSC, Woods Hole. 199 pp.

NMFS. 1993. Fishery management plan for sharks of the Atlantic Ocean. U.S. Dept. Comm., Washington DC. 261 pp.

Okera, W., J.D.Stevens & J.S. Gunn. 1981. Fishery situation report: Tropical sharks. Reprint No. 1216. CSIRO Mar. Lab. Austr. Govern. Publ. Serv., Canberra. pp. 59-72.

Olsen, A.M. 1954. The biology, migration, and growth rate of the school shark, Galeorhinus australis (Macleay) (Carcharhinidae) in south-eastern Australian waters. *Aust. J. Mar. Freshw. Res.* 5(3): 353-405.

Olsen, A.M. 1984. Synopsis of biological data on the school shark [Galeorhinus australis (Macleay 1881)]. FAO Fisheries Synopsis 139. FAO, Rome. 42 pp.

Otake, T. & K. Mizue. 1981. Direct evidence for oophagy in the thresher shark, *Alopias pelagicus*. *Jpn. J. Ichth.* 28: 171-172.

Parker, H.W. & F.C. Stott. 1965. Age, size and vertebral calcification in the basking shark, *Cetorhinus maximus* (Gunnerus). *Zool. Meded.* 40(34): 305-319.

Parsons, G.R. 1993. Age determination and growth of the bonnethead shark *Sphyrna tiburo*: a comparison of two populations. *Mar. Biol.* 117: 23-31.

Paust, B. & R. Smith. 1986. Salmon shark manual: The development of a commercial salmon shark, *Lamna ditropis*, fishery in the North Pacific. *Alaska Sea Grant Rep.* 86-01. Petersburg: 430 pp.

Pellegrin, G. 1996. By-catch estimates and estimates of relative abundance for sharks. Document SB-III-23. 1996 Shark Stock Assessment Workshop. NOAA/NMFS/SEFSC, Miami. 7 pp.

Phillips, J.B. 1948. Basking shark fishery revived in California. *Calif. Fish. Game, Fish Bull.* 134(1): 11-23.

Pollard, D.A. 1996. The biology and conservation status of the grey nurse shark [*Carcharias taurus* (Rafinesque 1810)] in New South Wales, Australia. *Aquatic Conservation: Marine and Freshwater Ecosystems* 6: 1-20.

Pratt, H.L. 1979. Reproduction in the blue shark, *Prionace glauca*. *U.S. Fish Wildl. Serv. Fish. Bull.* 77: 445-470.

Pratt, H.L. & J.G. Casey. 1983. Age and growth of the shortfin mako, *Isurus oxyrinchus*. *In* E.D. Prince & L.M. Pulos, eds. Proceedings of the international workshop on age determination of oceanic pelagic fishes: Tunas, billfishes, and sharks. NOAA Tech. Rep. NMFS 8: 175-177.

Pratt, H.L., Jr. & J.G. Casey. 1990. Shark reproductive strategies as a limiting factor in directed fisheries, with a review of Holden's method of estimating growth- parameters. *In* L.H. Pratt, S. Gruber & Y. Taniuchi, eds. Elasmobranchs as living resources. NOAA Technical Report 90. U.S. Dept. Comm., Washington DC. pp. 97-109.

Quero, J.C. & R. Emonnet. 1993. Disparition ou raréfaction d'espèces marines au large d'Archachon. Actes du III Colloque International "Océanographie du Golfe de Gascone". pp. 221-225.

Rae, B.B. 1962. Porbeagle sharks. *Dept. Ag. Fish., Scot. Fish. Bull.* 18: 17-18.

Ramachandran, A. & T.V. Sankar. 1990. Fins and fin rays from whale shark (*Rhiniodon typus* Smith). *Fish. Tech.* 27(2): 138-140.

Randall, J.E. 1986. *Sharks of Arabia.* Immel Publishing, London. 148 pp.

Rey, J.C. & E. Alot. 1984. Contribución al estudio de la pesqueria de palangre del pez espada (Xiphias gladius) en el Mediterraneo occidental. Collective Volume of Scientific Papers 20 (SCRS-1983), No. 2- Temperate Spp. ICCAT, Madrid. pp. 428-434.

Ripley, W.E. 1946. The soupfin shark and the fishery. *Calif. Dep. Fish. Game, Fish. Bull.* 64: 7-37.

Roedel, P.M. & W.M.E. Ripley. 1950. California sharks and rays. *Calif. Dep. Fish. Game, Fish. Bull.* 75: 1-88.

Rose, D.A. 1996. *An overview of world trade in sharks and other cartilaginous fishes.* TRAFFIC International, 106 p.

Russell, S.J. 1993. Shark bycatch in the Northern Gulf of Mexico tuna longline fishery, 1988-91, with observations on the near shore directed shark fishery. *In* S. Branstetter, ed. *Conservation Biology of elasmobranchs.* NOAA Technical Report NMFS 115: 19-29.

Schwartz, F.J. 1984. Occurrence, abundance and biology of the blacknose shark, *Carcharhinus acronotus* in North Carolina. *Northeast Gulf Sci.* 7 (1): 29-47.

Scott, G.P. 1996. Updated analysis of recent trends in catch rates of some Atlantic sharks. Document SBIII-17. 1996 Shark Stock Assessment Workshop. NOAA/NMFS/SEFSC, Miami. 18 pp.

Scott, G.P., P.J. Phares & B. Slater. 1996. Recreational catch, average size and effort for sharks in US Atlantic and Gulf of Mexico waters. Document SB-III-5. 1996 Shark Stock Assessment Workshop. NOAA/NMFS/SEFSC, Miami. 55 pp.

Seki, T., T. Taniuchi, H. Nakano & M. Shimizu. 1998. Age, growth and reproduction of the oceanic whitetip shark from the Pacific Ocean. *Fish. Sci.* 64: 14-20.

Setna, S.B. & P.N. Sarangdhar. 1949. Breeding habits of Bombay elasmobranchs. *Records of the Indian Museum.* Vol. 47: 107-124.

Shann, E.W. 1911. VIII- A description of the advanced embryonic stage of Lamna cornubica. *The 28th Annual Report of the Fishery Board for Scotland* 73- 79.

Silas, E.G. (ed.) 1986. The whale shark (*Rhiniodon typus* Smith) in Indian coastal waters: is the species endangered or vulnerable? *Mar. Fish. Infor. Serv. T & E Ser.* No. 66. Central Marine Fisheries Research Institute, Cochin. 38 pp.

Simpfendorfer, C. 1992. Biology of tiger sharks (*Galeocerdo cuvier*) caught by the Queensland shark meshing program off Townsville, Australia. *Aust. J. Mar. Freshw. Res.* 43: 33-43.

Sims, D.W., A.M. Fox & D.A. Merrett. 1997. Basking shark occurrence off south-west England in relation to zooplankton abundance. *J. Fish. Biol.* 51: 436-440.

Sims, D.W. and V.A. Quayle. 1998. Selective foraging behaviour of basking sharks on zooplankton in a small-scale front. *Nature* 393: 460-464.

Smith, S.E. 1984. Timing of vertebral-band deposition in tetracycline-injected leopard sharks. *Trans. Am. Fish. Soc.* 113: 308-313.

Sminkey, T.R. & J.A. Musick. 1995. Age and growth of the sandbar shark, *Carcharhinus plumbeus*, before and after population depletion. *Copeia* 1995: 871-883.

Snelson, F.F., Jr., T.J. Mulligan & S.E. Williams. 1984. Food habits, occurrence, and population structure of the bull shark, *Carcharhinus leucas*, in Florida coastal lagoons. *Bull. Mar. Sci.* 34: 71-80.

Springer, S. 1938. Notes on the sharks of Florida. *Proc. Florida Acad. Sci.* 3: 9-41.

Springer, S. 1948. Oviphagous embryos of the sand shark, *Carcharias taurus. Copeia* 1948: 153-157.

Springer, S. 1950a. An outline for a Trinidad shark fishery. *Proceedings of the Gulf and Caribbean Fisheries Institute. Second Annual Session.* Univ. of Miami, Coral Gables. pp. 17-26.

Springer, S. 1950b. Natural history notes on the lemon shark, *Negaprion brevirostris*. *Tex. J. Sci.* 3: 349-359.

Springer, S. 1950c. A revision of North American sharks allied to the genus Carcharhinus. *Am. Mus. Novit.* 1451. 13pp.

Springer, S. 1960. Natural history of the sandbar shark *Eulamia milberti*. *U.S. Fish. Wildl. Serv. Fish. Bull.* 61 (178): 1-38.

Springer, S. 1963. Field observations on large sharks of the Florida-Caribbean region. *In* P.W. Gilbert, ed. *Sharks and survival*. D.C. Heath and Co., Boston. pp. 95-113.

Springer, S. 1967. Social organizations of shark populations. *In* P.W. Gilbert, ed. *Sharks, skates, and rays*. John Hopkins Press, Baltimore. pp. 149-174.

Springer, S. 1979. Report on shark fishing in the western central Atlantic. WECAF report No. 3. UNDP. FAO. Panama. 39 pp.

Springer, S. and R.A. Waller. 1969. *Hexanchus vitulus*, a new sixgill shark from the Bahamas. *Bull. Mar. Sci.* 19: 159-174.

Squire, J.L. 1967. Observations of basking sharks and great white sharks in Monterey Bay, 1948-50. *Copeia* 1967: 247- 250.

Squire, J.L. 1990. Distribution and apparent abundance of the basking shark, *Cetorhinus maximus*, off the central and southern California Coast, 1962-85. *Mar. Fish. Rev.* 52(2): 7-11.

Stevens, J.D. (ed.). 1993. The status of chondricthyan resources in the southwest Pacific. Report of the South West Pacific Subgroup of the IUCN Shark Specialist Group. CSIRO Division of Fisheries, Tasmania. 49 pp.

Stevens, J.D. and J.M. Lyle. 1989. Biology of three hammerhead sharks (*Eusphyra blochii, Sphyrna mokarran*, and *S. lewini*) from northern Australia. *Aust. J. Mar. Freshw. Res.* 40: 129-146.

Stevens, J.D. & K.J. McLoughlin. 1991. Distribution, size, and sex composition, reproductive biology and diet of sharks from northern Australia. *Austr. J. Mar. Freshw. Res.* 42: 151-199.

Stevens, J.D. & P.D.Wiley. 1986. The biology of two commercially important carcharhinid sharks from northern Australia. *Aust. J. Mar. Freshw. Res.* 38: 701-710.

Strasburg, D.W. 1958. Distribution, abundance, and habits of pelagic sharks in the central Pacific Ocean. *U.S. Fish. Wildl. Serv. Fish. Bull.* 138 (58): 335-361.

Strong, W.R., Jr., R.C. Murphy, B.D. Bruce & D.R. Nelson. 1992. Movements and associated observations of bait-attracted white sharks, *Carcharodon carcharias*: a preliminary report. *Aust. J. Mar. Freshw. Res.* 43: 13-20.

Suda, A. 1953. Ecological study on the blue shark (*Prionace glauca*). South Seas Area Fisheries Research Laboratory, Report 26, Supplement 1. 15 pp.

Summers, G & R. Wong. 1992. Cosmetic products from semi-refined shark liver oil. Infofish International 2/92: 55-58.

Tachikawa, H. , T. Taniuchi & R. Arai. 1989. *Etmopterus baxteri*, a junior synonym of *E. granulosus* (Elasmobranchii, Squalidae). *Bull. Natl. Sci. Mus. Ser. A (Zool)* 15 (4): 235-241.

Tanaka, S. & K. Mizue. 1977. Studies on sharks- XI: Reproduction in female *Heptranchias perlo. Bull. Fac. Fish.* Nagasaki Univ. 42: 1-9.

Taniuchi, T. 1990. The role of elasmobranchs in Japanese fisheries. *In* H.L. Pratt, S. Gruber & T. Taniuchi, eds. *Elasmobranchs as living resources: Advances in the biology, ecology, systematics, and the status of the fisheries*. NOAA Technical Report NMFS 90. U.S. Dept. Comm., Washington DC. pp. 415-426.

Thorson, T.B. 1976. The status of the Lake Nicaragua shark: An updated appraisal. *In* T.B. Thorson, ed. *Investigations of the ichthyofauna of Nicaraguan lakes*. University of Nebraska-Lincoln, Lincoln. pp. 561-574.

Thorson, T.B. & E.J. Lacy. 1982. Age, growth rate and longevity of *Carcharhinus leucas* estimated from tagging and vertebral rings. *Copeia* 1982: 110-116.

Trono, R.B. 1996. Report on the preliminary investigation on the whale shark (*Rhincodon typus*) fishery in Bohol Sea, Philippines. WWF-Philippine Program: 25 pp.

Uchida, S., M. Toda, K. Teshima & K. Yano. 1996. Pregnant white sharks and full-term embryos from Japan. *In* A.P. Klimley and D.G. Ainley, eds. *Great white sharks: The biology of Carcharodon carcharias*. Academic Press, New York. pp. 139-155.

Ulrich, G.F. 1996. Fishery independent monitoring of large coastal sharks in South Carolina. 1996 Shark Stock Assessment Workshop. NOAA/NMFS/SEFSC, Miami: 16pp.

Urquhart, D.L. 1981. The North Pacific salmon shark. *Sea Frontiers* 27(6): 361-363.

Vas, P. 1990. The abundance of the blue shark, *Prionace glauca*, in the western English channel. *Environ. Biol. Fishes* 29: 209-225.

Walford, L.A. 1935. The sharks and rays of California. *Calif. Dep. Fish. Game, Fish. Bull.* 45: 1-66.

Walker, T. 1995a. Gummy shark 1995. Stock Assesment Report, Southern Shark Fishery Assessment Group. Australian Fisheries Management Authority, Canberra. 33 pp.

Walker, T. 1995b. School shark 1995. Stock Assessment Report, Southern Shark Fishery Assessment Group. Australian Fisheries Management Authority, Canberra. 38 pp.

Walker, T., T. Stone, T. Battaglene & K. McLoughlin. 1996a. The Southern Shark Fishery 1995. Fisheries Assessment Report, Southern Shark Fishery Assessment Group. Australian Fisheries Management Authority, Canberra. 55 pp.

Walker, T., B.L. Taylor, R.J. Hudson & T.M. Bath. 1996b. Catch and effort in the Southern Shark Fishery during 1970-95. Southern Shark Assesment Group. Australian Fisheries Management Authority, Canberra. 29 pp.

Walter, J.P. & D.A. Ebert. 1991. Preliminary estimates of age of the bronze whaler *Carcharhinus brachyurus* (Chondrichthyes: Carcharhinidae) from southern Africa, with a review of some life history parameters. *S. Afr. J. Mar. Sci.* 10: 37- 44.

Wetherbee, B.M., G.L. Crow & C.G. Lowe. 1996. Biology of the Galapagos shark, *Carcharhinus galapagensis*, in Hawaii. *Environ. Biol. Fishes* 45: 299-310.

Westrheim, S.J. 1950. The soupfin shark fishery of Oregon. *Fish Comm. Res. Briefs (Oregon)* 3 (10): 39-49.

Wintner, S.B. and G. Cliff. 1996. Age and growth determination of the blacktip shark, *Carcharhinus limbatus*, from the east coast of South Africa. *U.S. Fish Wildl. Serv. Fish. Bull.* 94:135-144.

7. Species Index